FRISKY PHONICS FUN 2

Written and illustrated
by Barbara Bachman

Cover design by Barbara Bachman
Cover by Tom Sjoerdsma
Copyright © Good Apple, Inc., 1984
Printing No. 987654321
ISBN No. 0-86653-212-9

GOOD APPLE, INC.
BOX 299
CARTHAGE, IL 62321-0299

Table of Contents

A Letter to the Teacher

Dear Teacher:

If you are looking for a comprehensive phonics workbook that captures and "keeps" student interest, then *Frisky Phonics Fun* is for you! Through a host of reproducible and beautifully illustrated discussion pages, activities, games, and performance work sheets, you will cultivate the application of phonics in a way that will fascinate the beginning reader!

If you have already met our five frisky friends in Book One, you have seen these clever hosts entertain the entire classroom as they help you to ensure the sufficient student mastery of basic word-attack skills.

A child can begin Book Two *after* he/she has mastered single-consonant sounds*, consonant blends*, consonant digraphs*, and short vowel sounds* (*all covered in Book One).

When a student is fairly confident with reading and spelling one-syllable words that have short vowel sounds, he/she is ready for Book Two.

Frisky Phonics Fun 2 introduces valuable spelling secrets as students learn and work with:

1. **2-Syllable and Compound Words**
2. **Plurals**
3. **Word Endings**
     (__er, __est, __en, __ing, __ed, __le, __y)
4. **R-Controlled Vowels**
     (er, ir, ur, or, ar)
5. **Long Vowel Sounds**
6. **The "Magic" E**
     (consonant-vowel-consonant-e words)
7. **Vowel Digraphs**
     (ee, ea /ē/; oa /ō/; ai, ay /ā/; oo; ow /ō/; ey /ē/)
8. **Vowel Diphthongs and Other Vowel Combinations**
     (ou, ow /ou/; au, aw /ô/; oi, oy /oi/; y /ī/)
9. **Open Syllable Words**
     (long vowel sounds in syllable division)

We wish you much happiness with *Frisky Phonics Fun 2* as you continue to enrich your creative teaching endeavors!

Barbara Bachman
and
The Friendly Folks at Good Apple, Inc.

A Special Spelling Secret

Plural means **more than one thing.**
Words can be plural.
When a word tells us about more than one thing, it
is plural.

cat

cats

This is a plural word : **cats**.
We must add an **_s** to most
words when we are talking
about <u>more</u> than just
one thing.

cat cats	bug bugs	frog frogs	sock socks

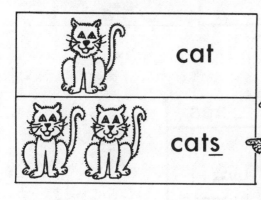

brush

brushes

This is a plural word : **brushes**.
We are talking about <u>more</u> than
just one brush.
We must add an **_es** to
words that end with
<u>sh</u>, <u>ch</u>, <u>s</u>, <u>x</u>, or <u>z</u>.

brush brushes	dish dishes	match matches	class classes	box boxes	buzz buzzes

Words to Read and Spell

Adding __s

flag	pet	kid	dog	bug
flags	pets	kids	dogs	bugs
plant	step	gift	sock	truck
plants	steps	gifts	socks	trucks
hand	belt	brick	song	duck
hands	belts	bricks	songs	ducks

__s

Adding __es

__ches	__shes	__ses	__xes	__zes
bench	wish	bus	box	buzz
benches	wishes	buses	boxes	buzzes
match	brush	glass	fox	quiz
matches	brushes	glasses	foxes	quizzes
crutch	dish	kiss	ax	
crutches	dishes	kisses	axes	
stitch	ash	dress	tax	
stitches	ashes	dresses	taxes	
branch	flash	class	six	
branches	flashes	classes	sixes	

__es

DOGGONE EXCEPTIONS	
man	elf
men	elves
ox	shelf
oxen	shelves

2

Drinks and Snacks at Mr. Bob's

NAME _____ DATE _____

Come join the dogs for drinks and snacks at Mr. Bob's! Run down the Tree Stump Pass to the snack stand. You must circle the word that names each picture along the way.

Dogtown's Summer Grabs!

NAME _____   DATE _____

Please help the **Dogtown Daily** newspaper! They must finish all the ads for Dogtown's Summer Grabs Sale. Lots of shops will be having big summer sales and they want their ads printed fast! Fill in all the blanks you see with an __s or __es.

DOGTOWN POST OFFICE
SALE! ON ALL
stamp____ and box____

The Pottery Shack
dish____
mug____
glass____
All ½ Price!

The Looking Glass
SALE!!
All glass____ 50% Off!

The Bath Hut
SALE ON ALL
dog brush____

Dixie's Best Dress Shop
Everything On SALE!!
dress____
sock____
belt____
vest____

Dogtown Jewelry
ring____ $3.99
cross____ $4

Dogtown Lumber
Sale!
log____ ....20% off
ax____ ...30% off
red brick____ .....50% off

TOM'S PATIO STUFF
Sale!! On all
plant____
and
bench____

4

What's on the TV?

NAME _____

DATE _____

On every TV below, you will see a picture. Write the word that names each picture. Your words will end with __s or __es. Tell us what's on the TV!

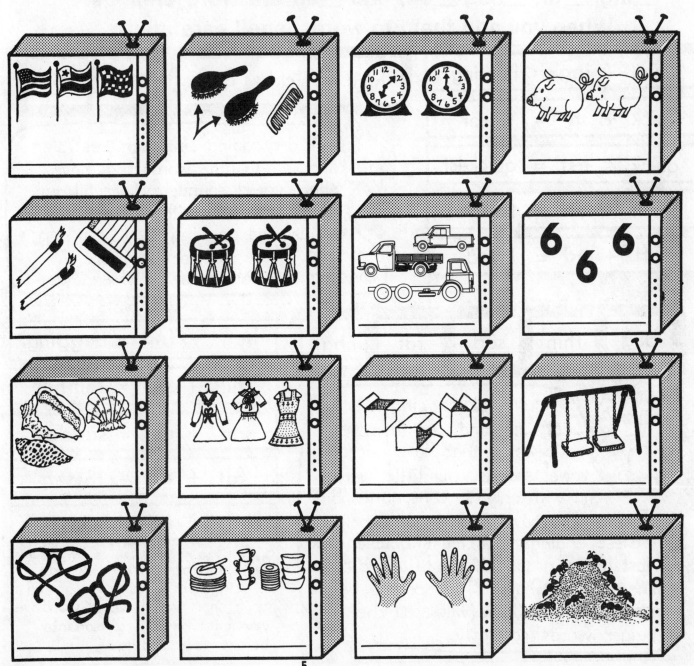

A Special Spelling Secret

_ing, _er, _est, _en, and _ed are word endings.
When you add them to words, spell carefully!

hunt + **ing** = hunting	hŭn**t** sĭ**ck** quĭ**ck** frĕ**sh** lĭ**ft**

hunt + **ing** = hunting

sick + **er** = sicker

quick + **est** = quickest

fresh + **en** = freshen

lift + **ed** = lifted

We are adding **_ing, _er, _est, _en** and **_ed** to little words that have short vowel sounds. Since all our little words end with **2** consonants, we just add on _ing, _er, _est, _en, or _ed. There should always be **2** consonants before these word endings.

bĕg thĭ**n** să**d** fă**t** chă**t**

We are adding **_ing, _er, _est, _en,** and **_ed** to more little words that have short vowel sounds. Our little words end with only **1** consonant. But we should have **2** consonants before these endings. We must **double the last letter** in each of our little words. Then we will have **2** consonants before each ending, and we will spell the bigger words correctly.

beg + **ing** = begging

thin + **er** = thinner

sad + **est** = saddest

fat + **en** = fatten

chat + **ed** = chatted

Remember: When you add _ing, _er, _est, _en, or _ed to a short vowel sound word, you must have 2 consonants before each ending.

Words to Read and Spell

big	fresh	winner	winning
bigger	fresher	runner	running
biggest	freshest	swimmer	swimming
mad	sick		
madder	sicker	pitcher	pitching
maddest	sickest	catcher	catching
	sicken	kicker	kicking
fat		hunter	hunting
fatter	long	helper	helping
fattest	longer	camper	camping
fatten	longest	singer	singing

ladder	slipper	offer
matter	zipper	robber
after	dinner	locker
cracker	bitter	cobbler
master	litter	
anger	sister	under
hanger	winter	supper
	whisper	summer
better	silver	rubber
letter	finger	blubber
dresser		butter
pepper	other	shutter
	another	suffer
	brother	
shelter	mother	bumper
member	father	thunder
blender	together	hunger
temper		

happen	bitten
fasten	kitten
	mitten
often	
rotten	
gotten	kitchen
pollen	children
	chicken

DOGGONE EXCEPTIONS		
river	ever	proper
liver	never	boxer
quiver	clever	mixer
shiver	seven	boxing
		mixing

7

Stamping Stickers on the Bumpers of Buses

NAME _____ **DATE** _____

On the back doors of every bus below, you will see a word with a short vowel sound. You will also see a word ending. Add the endings to the words and spell carefully! Print your words on the bumper stickers.

Spelling Words on Winter Slippers

NAME _____

DATE _____

On every slipper below, you will see 2 word endings. On every dog's ankle, you will see a word. Add each of the endings to the word. Spell 2 new words! Read your words to your teacher!

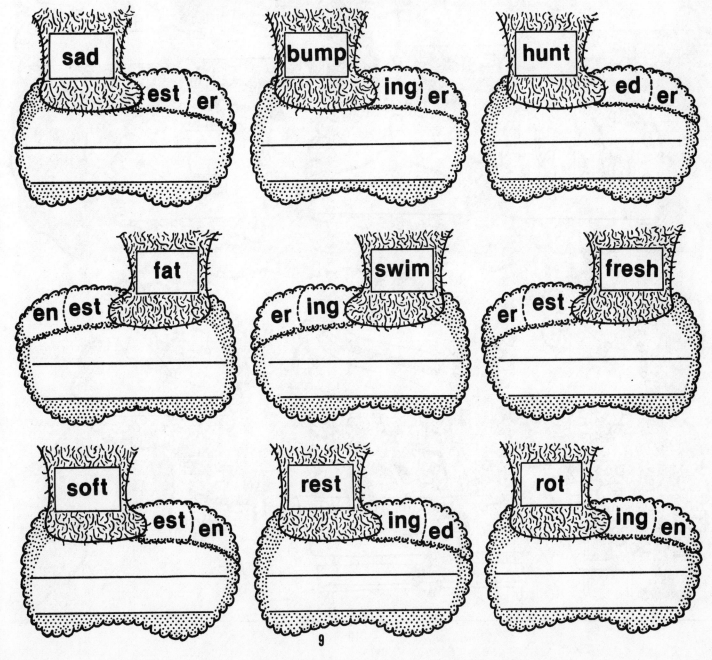

sad   est er

bump   ing er

hunt   ed er

fat   en est

swim   er ing

fresh   er est

soft   est en

rest   ing ed

rot   ing en

A Chicken Dinner on the Dogtown River!

NAME _____ DATE _____

 Come join the dogs for a chicken dinner on the Dogtown River! Follow the trees and write the word that names each picture along the way.

 # Butter ? Stumpers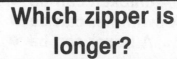

NAME _____ **DATE** _____

🐾 Can you answer a butter stumper? On every stick of butter below, you will see a question. You will also see 2 pictures. Circle the picture that will answer each question.

Which sister is thinner?

Which zipper is longer?

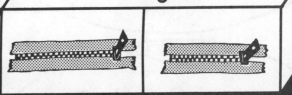

Which kitten is fatter?

Which blender is mixing?

Which letter is for Mr. Masters?

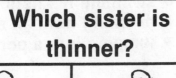

Which ram is madder?

Which lifter is stronger?

Which banker is richer?

Passing, Catching and Matching!

NAME _____   DATE _____

In each row of footballs, you will see parts of sentences. Draw lines from dot to dot and connect the sentence parts that match!

A chicken can be ●
A swimmer can be ●
A boxer can be ●

● swinging his fists.
● hatching from an egg.
● jumping into a pond.

A runner can be ●
A camper can be ●
A golfer can be ●

● packing a trunk.
● jogging on a track.
● swinging his clubs.

A shopper can be ●
A kitten can be ●
A duck can be ●

● quacking and running.
● getting eggs and butter.
● resting on a rug.

Chicken dinners can be ●
A bunch of hands can be ●
Six clocks can be ●

● clapping
● sitting on hot platters.
● ticking.

A man can be ●
A robber can be ●
A mixer can be ●

● asking for cash.
● stepping on a ladder.
● blending a batter.

12

LET'S TALK ABOUT
the <u>3</u> Sounds of _ed

__ed is a word ending.

We add __ed to action words when the "action" has already happened.

__ed can say /ed/, /d/, or /t/.

_ed can say /ĕd/

ĕd

land	chat
landed	chatted
melt	rest
melted	rested
dust	plant
dusted	planted

_ed can say /d/

d

spell	rob
spelled	robbed
grab	fill
grabbed	filled
plan	yell
planned	yelled

_ed can say /t/

t

mop	bump
mopped	bumped
pinch	crash
pinched	crashed
wink	check
winked	checked

13

WANTED: Fat Caterpillars!

NAME _____ DATE _____

Help! Fat caterpillars are licking up all of Dogtown's potted plants! They must be hunted down and marked with a red X. Then they can be shipped back to Dogtown's Caterpillar Shack! On every caterpillar below, you will see a word that ends with __ed. The __ed will say /ed/, /d/, or /t/. Put a red X on the right ending sound for each word. Thanks for your help!

| melted | ed | d | t | | ed | d | t | stopped |

| pinched | ed | d | t | | ed | d | t | wilted |

| spelled | ed | d | t | | ed | d | t | kissed |

| brushed | ed | d | t | | ed | d | t | planted |

| bumped | ed | d | t | | ed | d | t | grabbed |

| dusted | ed | d | t | | ed | d | t | yelled |

14

A ZIPPER TWISTER!

Pinned, Stitched, and Mended Zips

YOU WILL NEED: 2 players

2 gameboard markers

a gameboard (on page 16)

18 PINNED cards (on page 17)

18 STITCHED cards (on page 18)

18 MENDED cards (on page 19)

One space on the gameboard is between every two pins!

1.	Look at the gameboard. Two players will race down the zipper to the "Winner" space.
2.	Look at the game cards. They have sentences on them. All the __ed words on the "Pinned" cards will end with a /d/ sound. The __ed words on the "Stitched" cards will end with a /t/ sound. The __ed words on the "Mended" cards will end with the /ed/ sound. Cut out all the cards. Put them in 3 piles face down on the appropriate gameboard boxes.
3.	**Player #1:** Put your marker on the first PINNED space. Draw a PINNED card. Read the sentence. Player #2 will check you. If you read all the words correctly, COUNT THE PINS on your card and move ahead that many spaces. If you do NOT read the words correctly, STAY where you are; you will draw another card from this deck on your next turn. **Player #2:** Now you do the same.
4.	Take turns moving down the gameboard. If you land on a STITCHED space, draw and read a STITCHED card. You will count stitches to move forward. If you land on a MENDED space, draw and read a MENDED card. You will count needles to move forward.

A ZIPPER TWISTER!
Pinned, Stitched, and Mended Zips

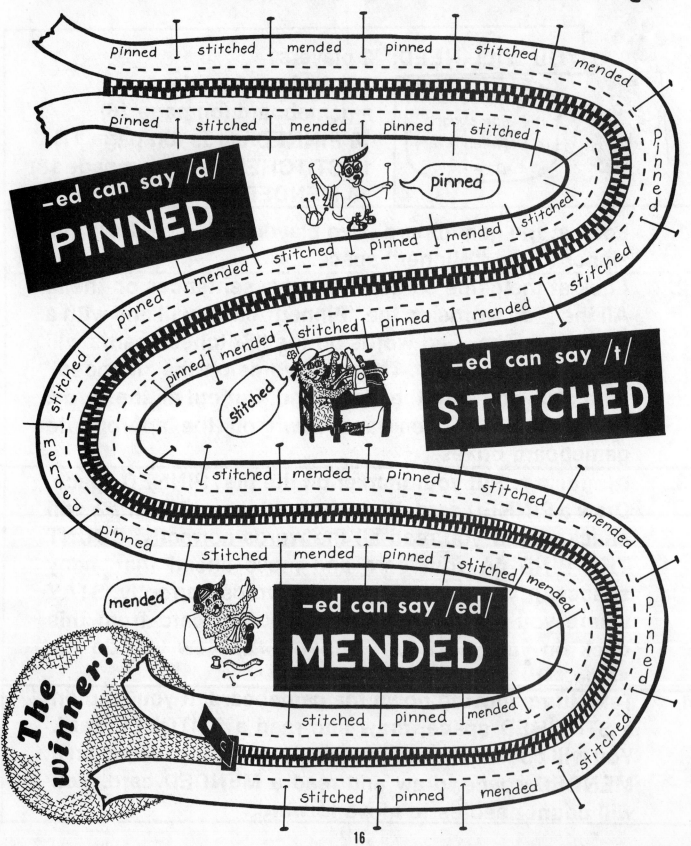

A ZIPPER TWISTER!

Pinned, Stitched, and Mended Zips

(Pinned Cards)

Dad grilled hot dogs and buns for lunch.	Mom was thrilled when she got a gift from her sister.	A sled can be dragged up a big hill.
The runner hummed a song as he jogged.	Sam scrubbed his pots and pans with stiff brushes.	The man spilled his drink on his vest.
The dog wagged his tail when he was glad.	The winner grinned and yelled when he got the red ribbon.	Clocks can be plugged in.
To help Mom fix dinner, we shelled shrimp.	A doll can be hugged.	A fishing net can be grabbed fast.
A word can be spelled.	Tom filled in the blanks on his spelling test.	Fun summer trips can be planned.
Beth filled six glasses with milk.	A big pitcher of punch can be chilled.	The dog begged when he smelled a fresh snack.

A ZIPPER TWISTER!
Pinned, Stitched, and Mended Zips
(Stitched Cards)

Dan zipped up his winter vest. —	Dad rushed to the bank and got his check cashed. — —	Jack stepped on a crab and got pinched. — —
Rats can be tricked by fast traps. —	The truck stopped fast and crashed. — —	The glass cracked when Bess dropped it. —
Your lips can get chapped in the winter wind. — —	Bob stepped up the ladder and picked fresh plums. — ‖	Nan passed the pepper to her sister. — —
Sam ripped his pants when he fell. —	The stockings were stuffed with lots of gifts. — —	The children jumped and splashed into the river. — — —
Mother thanked us for helping her. —	Jill clapped her hands and snapped her fingers. — — —	A bad dog can get spanked. —
Spelling tests can be checked. —	He slipped in the mud and bumped his leg on a big rock. — — ‖	After Jim packed his trunk, he locked it. — —

A ZIPPER TWISTER!
Pinned, Stitched, and Mended Zips
(Mended Cards)

The rubber raft drifted across the river.	Ben lifted the big box and set it on a shelf.	The butter melted as the pan got hotter.
The plant wilted in the hot sun.	Mom printed her list on a pad.	A robber cannot be trusted.
We were glad when the sad song ended.	Max dusted the shelf with a soft rag.	We went on a camping trip that lasted ten days.
Ted hunted and hunted for his lost kitten.	A big bug landed on Jim's leg.	Rob handed a bunch of cash to his sister.
A bad rip can be mended with a patch.	An ox on a ranch will be branded.	A dog's back can be spotted.
Beth lifted her chin and nodded.	The math class ended when the bell rang.	After Pam had a nap, she felt rested.

LET'S TALK ABOUT
Syllables and Compound Words

Syllables are **word parts.**
A word can have 1 or more parts.
A word can have 1 or more syllables.

frog	plums
fish	pets

These are **1-part** words.
Each word has **1 syllable.**

but•ter	hun•dred
butter	hundred
mit•ten	prob•lem
mitten	problem

These are **2-part** words.
Each word has **2 syllables.**

fan•tas•tic	won•der•ful
fantastic	wonderful

These are **3-part** words.
Each word has **3 syllables.**

Compound words are **2 whole words**
put together and spelled as **1 big word.**

dust•pan	grass•hopper	finger•print
dustpan	grasshopper	fingerprint

Words to Read and Spell

__et

jacket   comet
racket   bonnet
basket   pocket
blanket   rocket
hatchet   socket
tablet   locket
magnet   closet
   goblet

helmet
velvet   bucket
   trumpet
cricket   puppet
ticket
skillet

__it

rabbit
habit
bandit
admit
commit

exit

visit

pulpit

__ish

radish
Spanish

English
selfish

finish

polish

punish
publish

__ic

attic
traffic
panic
plastic

public

picnic

__ness

sadness
illness
witness
sickness

__on

cannon
gallon
wagon

lemon
lesson
melon

ribbon

cotton

button

__in

cabin
satin
napkin

coffin
robin
bobbin
goblin

muffin
pumpkin

__el

tassel
travel
gravel
panel
camel

level
kennel

nickel

model
novel
tunnel

__al

petal   sandal
metal
pedal   signal
medal   hospital

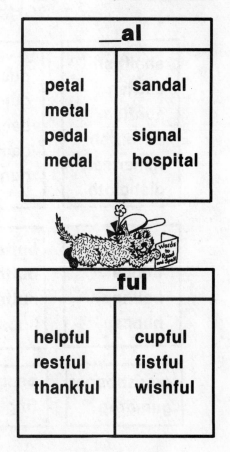

__ful

helpful   cupful
restful   fistful
thankful   wishful

Words to Read and Spell

problem
seldom
kingdom
blossom
tantrum

invent
insult
inspect
insect
insist
dentist
contest

district
dismiss
discuss
discover
misspell

address
unless
undress
confess
helpless
tennis
cactus
octopus

itself
himself
hundred
husband

salad
method

wonderful
fantastic

upset
expect
suspect
subject
subtract

command
understand
telegram

September
helicopter

Compound Words

shellfish
catfish
sunfish
silverfish
fisherman
dishcloth

dustpan
quicksand
backhand
backpack
hunchback

checkup
chipmunk
Chap Stick
lipstick
drumstick

sandbag
sandbox
sandwich
handcuffs
cuff links

bobsled
bobcat
bellhop
hubcap

buttercup
buttermilk
butterscotch
hopscotch

popgun
shotgun
slingshot
cannot

eggshell
nutshell
nutcracker

grasshopper
gumdrop

peppermint
fingerprint

suntan
sunset
sunglasses

windmill
standstill
stepladder

What's on the Tablet?

NAME _____

DATE _____

🐾 On every tablet below, you will see a picture. Write the word that names each picture. Choose your answers from the word boxes.

cannon ribbon button	_____	_____	_____
puppet helmet basket	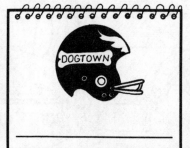_____	_____	_____
pumpkin napkin cabin	_____	_____	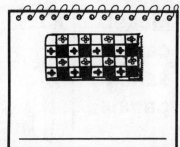_____
rabbit racket jacket	_____	_____	_____

Shovels and Buckets

NAME _____   DATE _____

On every shovel below, you will see a picture. In the long box, you will see a list of words. Find and write the word that names each picture. Print your words on the buckets!

trumpet
cricket
pocket
skillet
hatchet
blanket

nickel
camel
sandal
pedals

lemon
wagon

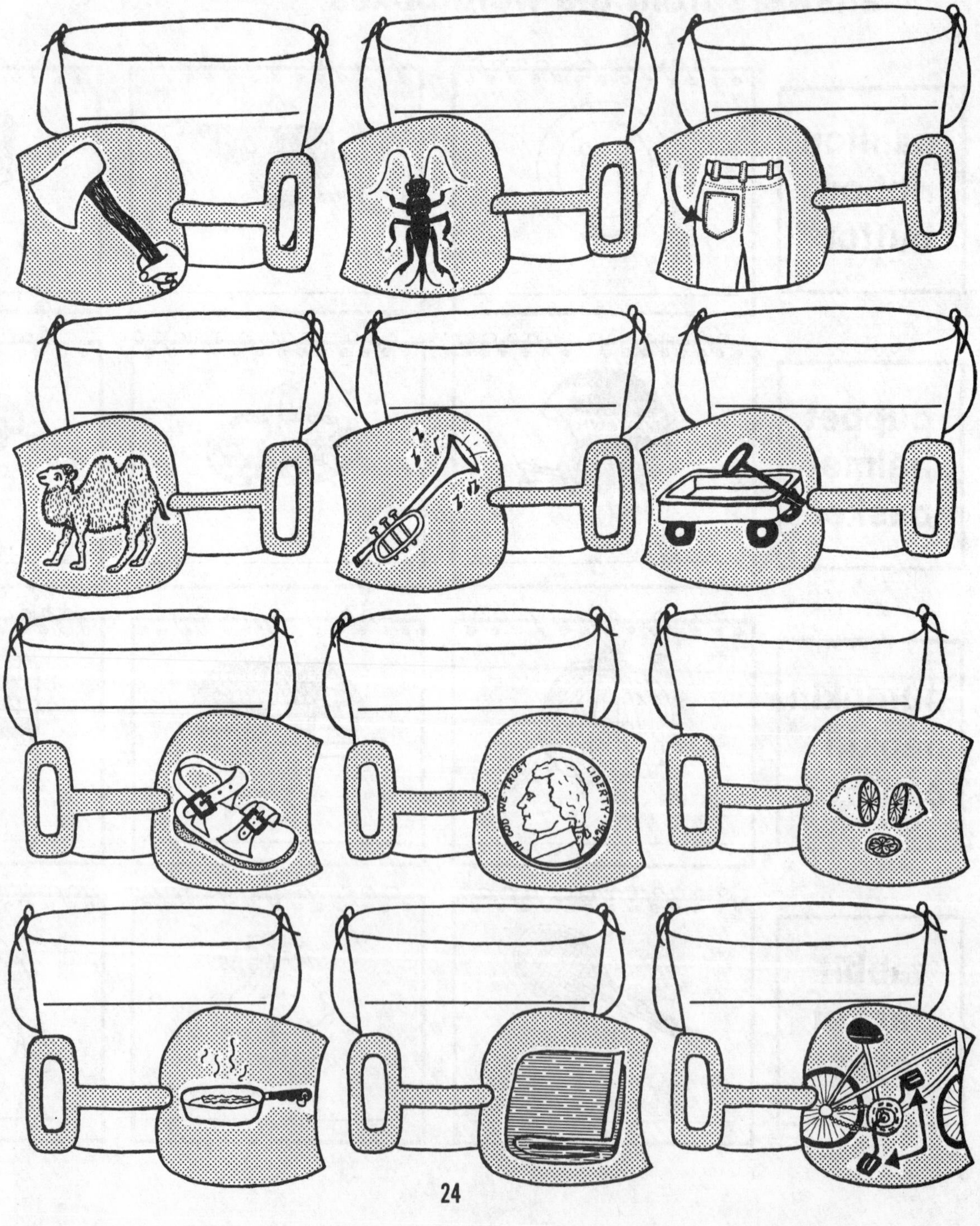

24

CATEGORIES

 Underline all the things below that you might find in a closet.

belts	a quacking crab	slippers
dresses	a winter jacket	hangers
frogs	a grinning log	a cricket
boxes	a rotten plum	sandals
a vest	a tennis racket	rabbits
a river	a red blanket	a helmet
a pig	shocking thunder	a coffin
a cabin	a honking truck	golf clubs

 Underline all the things below that you might find in a kitchen.

napkins	cops and robbers	a mixer
crackers	pots and pans	a blender
monsters	mugs and cups	a nest
dishes	plastic bags	a clock
pepper	a gas pump	a skillet
eggs	a shopping list	a sifter
butter	a mop bucket	a camel
hogs	a dishcloth	a snack
lunch	a gallon of milk	a cannon
a tent	a picnic basket	a pitcher
glasses	a trash can	a sink

Two on a Tandem!

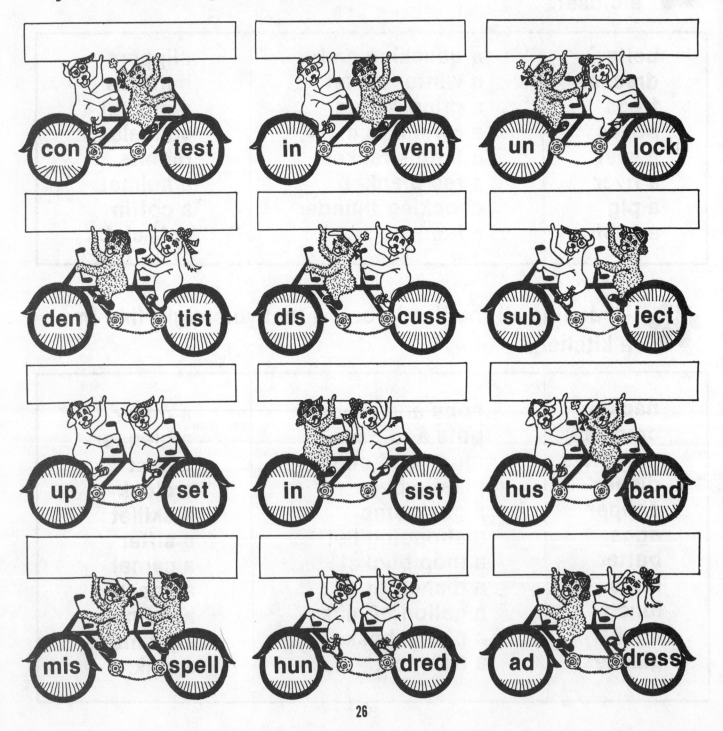

NAME _____   DATE _____

On the wheels of every tandem bicycle below, you will see 2 word parts. Add the word parts together and spell a 2-syllable word! Write your words in the boxes. Read all your words to your teacher!

con | test

in | vent

un | lock

den | tist

dis | cuss

sub | ject

up | set

in | sist

hus | band

mis | spell

hun | dred

ad | dress

Syllables on Eggshells and Muffins

NAME _____ DATE _____

🐾 All of the eggshells and muffins below have words on them. Each word will have 1, 2, or 3 syllables. Tell us how many syllables are in each word. Circle 1, 2, or 3.

dogs 1 2 3   visit 1 2 3   king 1 2 3   salad 1 2 3   brush 1 2 3   glasses 1 2 3

sister 1 2 3   tennis 1 2 3   cotton 1 2 3   upset 1 2 3   magnet 1 2 3   whisper 1 2 3

discover 1 2 3   helpful 1 2 3   children 1 2 3   discuss 1 2 3

thunder 1 2 3   telegram 1 2 3   wonderful 1 2 3   fantastic 1 2 3

ticket 1 2 3   finish 1 2 3   happen 1 2 3   traffic 1 2 3   ducks 1 2 3   signal 1 2 3

matches 1 2 3   trash 1 2 3   contest 1 2 3   subject 1 2 3   witness 1 2 3   tunnel 1 2 3

Over the Net with a Backhand Shot!

NAME _____ **DATE** _____

Come join the dogs for a spelling game of Ping-Pong! To win each game, you must add together the 2 words on every table to spell 1 big compound word! Write your compound words in the spaces above the nets. Get over that net with a backhand shot! Read all your words to your teacher!

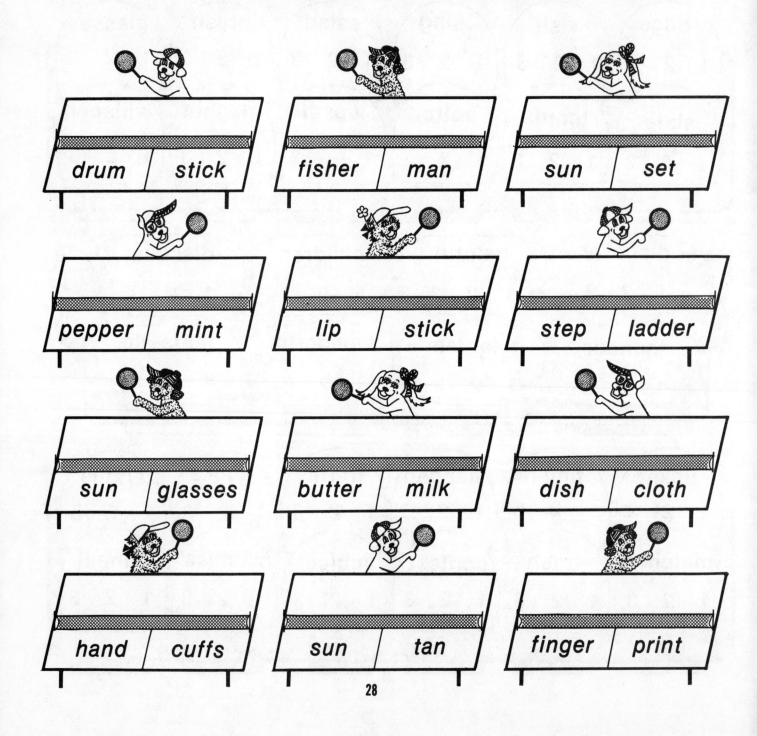

| drum | stick | | fisher | man | | sun | set |

| pepper | mint | | lip | stick | | step | ladder |

| sun | glasses | | butter | milk | | dish | cloth |

| hand | cuffs | | sun | tan | | finger | print |

28

What's Happening?

NAME _____ DATE _____

Each sentence below will tell us what is happening in one of the pictures. The sentences are numbered. Put the right sentence number in the corner box of each matching picture.

1. Sam got this ribbon for winning the contest.
2. The fisherman will have lemon muffins and this chicken salad sandwich for lunch.
3. This math problem is asking us to subtract ten from one hundred.
4. This chipmunk has on sunglasses and lipstick!
5. Mom printed Mr. Black's address on this letter.
6. The dentist is giving this dog a checkup.
7. After the children finish dinner, they can have this sack of gumdrops!
8. This grasshopper is licking a peppermint stick!

Endings

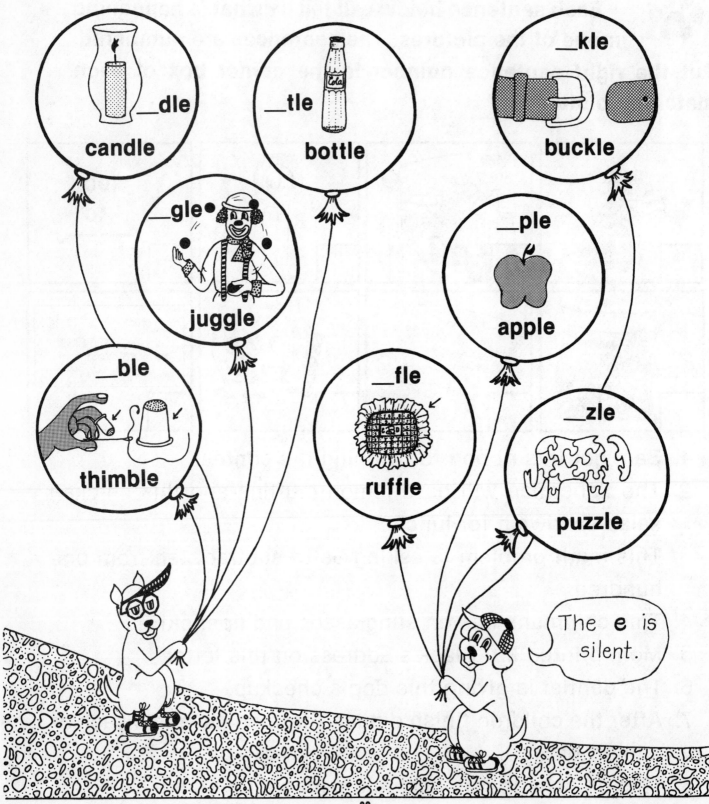

The e is silent.

30

Words to Read and Spell

__ble
gamble
scramble

pebble

nibble
dribble
thimble

gobble

bubble
mumble
tumble
rumble
fumble
crumble
stumble

__dle
paddle
saddle
candle
handle

middle
fiddle
riddle

puddle
cuddle
huddle
bundle

__kle
tackle
crackle

freckle

pickle
tickle
trickle
twinkle
sprinkle

buckle
chuckle

__gle
angle
tangle
dangle
strangle

wiggle
jiggle
giggle
single
tingle
mingle
shingle

jungle
juggle
snuggle
struggle

__cle
uncle

__tle
battle
tattle
rattle

kettle
settle

little

bottle

__ple
apple

temple
dimple
ripple
simple

__zle
dazzle

sizzle

guzzle
puzzle

__fle
ruffle
shuffle

raffle

sniffle

Nibble on a Rhyming Apple!

NAME _____ DATE _____

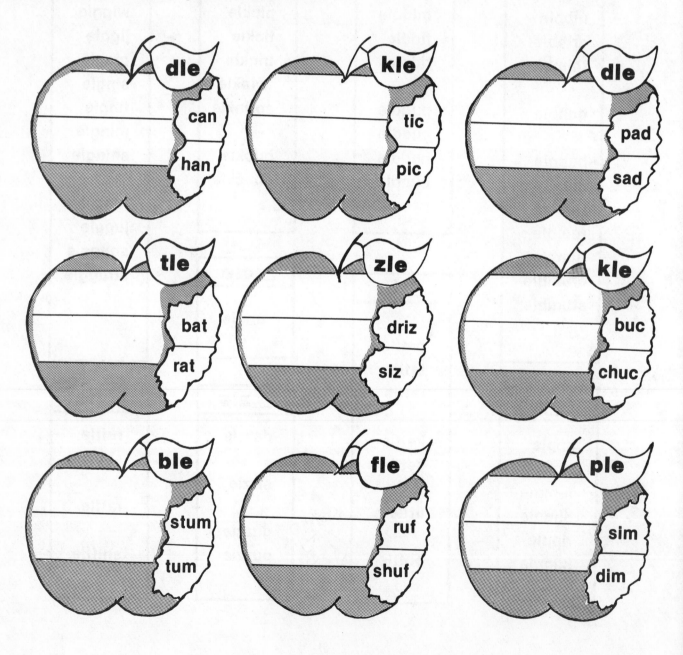

On every apple leaf below, you will see a word ending. Inside each apple, you will see 2 beginning syllables. Add the ending to each of the beginning syllables and spell 2 rhyming words! Write your words in the blank spaces. Read all your words to your teacher!

dle — can, han

kle — tic, pic

dle — pad, sad

tle — bat, rat

zle — driz, siz

kle — buc, chuc

ble — stum, tum

fle — ruf, shuf

ple — sim, dim

Matching Puzzles to Simple Little Riddles

NAME _____ DATE _____

Get ready to answer riddles with puzzles! Read every riddle and find the puzzle that will answer it. Then you must write the words that answer the riddles. Print your words on the blanks.

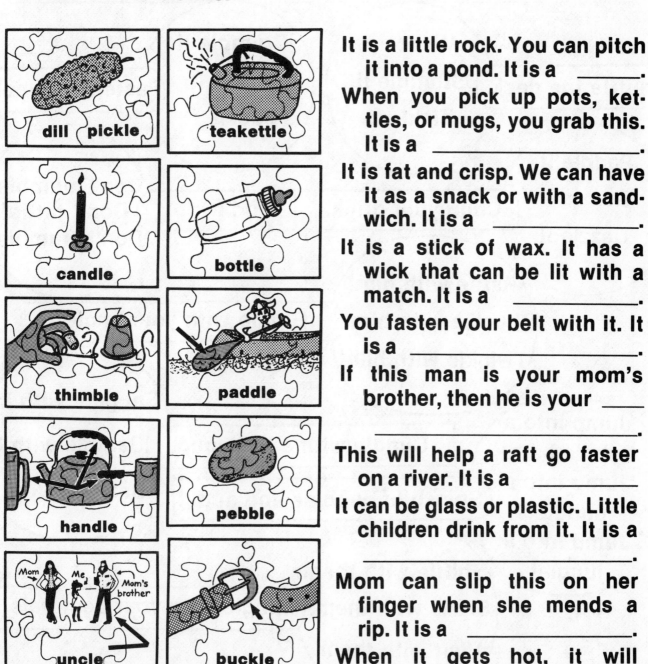

dill pickle

teakettle

candle

bottle

thimble

paddle

handle

pebble

Mom   Me   Mom's brother

uncle

buckle

It is a little rock. You can pitch it into a pond. It is a _____.

When you pick up pots, kettles, or mugs, you grab this. It is a _____.

It is fat and crisp. We can have it as a snack or with a sandwich. It is a _____.

It is a stick of wax. It has a wick that can be lit with a match. It is a _____.

You fasten your belt with it. It is a _____.

If this man is your mom's brother, then he is your ____ _____.

This will help a raft go faster on a river. It is a _____.

It can be glass or plastic. Little children drink from it. It is a _____.

Mom can slip this on her finger when she mends a rip. It is a _____.

When it gets hot, it will whistle! It is a _____.

33

Dogtown's Lollipop Jingles

NAME _____ DATE _____

🐾 Can you answer a lollipop jingle? First read the
sentence on the lollipop stick. Then find a sentence on the
lollipop that means the same thing and underline it!

Mix it up.
Strangle it.
Tickle it.

Shuffle the deck.

Crumble it.
Pickle it.
Buckle it.

Fasten your belt.

Paddle it.
Guzzle it.
Dazzle it.

Chug your drink.

Don't trip!

Don't mumble!
Don't tattle!
Don't stumble!

Rattle with him!
Chuckle with him!
Twinkle with him!

Giggle with your uncle!

Snuggle with it.
Gamble with it.
Battle with it.

Cuddle with a little pup.

Jump into a
bubble bath!
Jump into a
puddle!
Jump into a
jungle!

Splash in bubbles and suds!

Sniffle with them.
Sizzle with them.
Visit with them.

Mingle with your best pals.

34

Endings

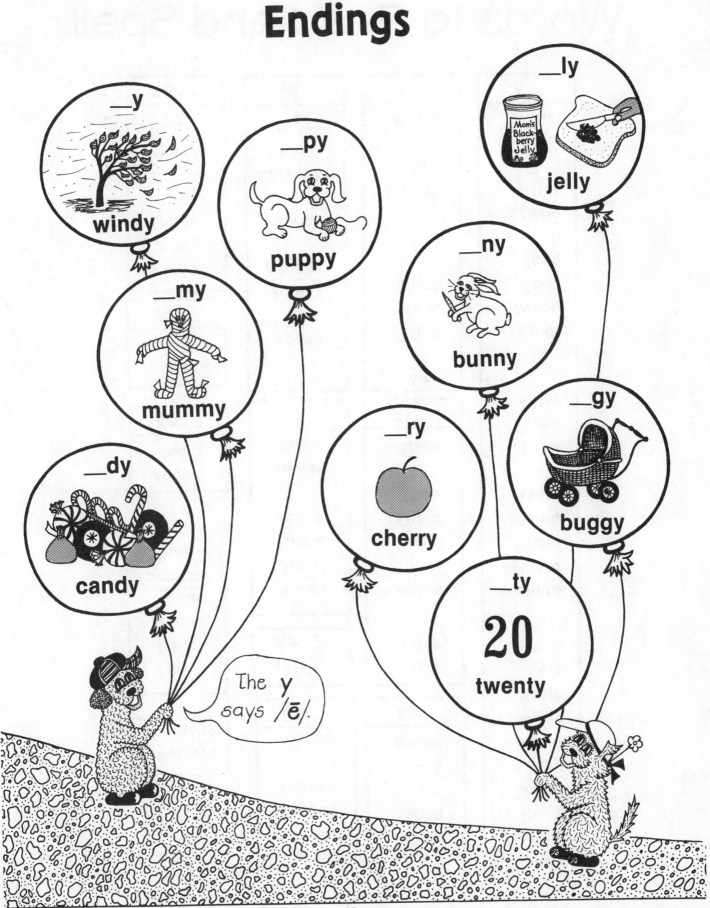

__ly
jelly

__y
windy

__py
puppy

__my
mummy

__ny
bunny

__gy
buggy

__dy
candy

__ry
cherry

__ty
20
twenty

The y says /ē/.

35

Words to Read and Spell

__y	__ly	__py	__gy
any	gladly	happy	shaggy
many		snappy	baggy
	silly	unhappy	
very	quickly		foggy
messy		peppy	soggy
	jelly		
body		choppy	buggy
copy	softly	sloppy	
bossy	holly		
rocky	jolly	puppy	

__ry
cherry
berry

__ty	__ny	__by
nasty	penny	lobby
	skinny	hobby
empty		
pretty	sunny	
plenty	bunny	
twenty	runny	
seventy	funny	

tacky
sandy
handy

fussy
bumpy
jumpy
grumpy
crunchy

hilly · sixty
silky · fifty
picky

__zy
dizzy

angry
hungry
simply
pantry

sticky

__dy	__my
daddy	mommy
candy	
	yummy
buddy	tummy
muddy	mummy

tricky
risky
frisky
windy
slippery

anything
blackberry

Rhyming Words on a Puppy Buggy!

NAME _____ DATE _____

On every puppy buggy below, you will see a word ending. Each dog is holding 2 beginning syllables. Add the word ending to each of the beginning syllables and spell 2 rhyming words! Write your words on the buggy.

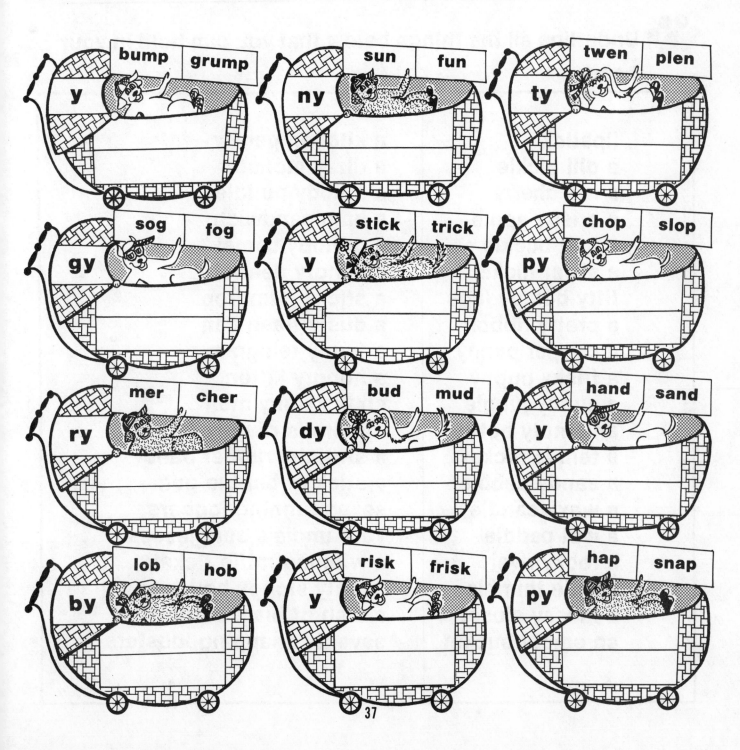

CATEGORIES

NAME _____ DATE _____

 Underline all the things below that you can hold in your hand.

lipstick	a kitchen pantry
a dill pickle	a dizzy monster
a red cherry	a muddy puddle
a crispy apple	a ham sandwich
a belt buckle	a grumpy camel
a silver nickel	an angry dentist
fifty bumpy logs	a sticky gumdrop
a pretty ribbon	a dusty trash can
a copper penny	a funny telegram
a frisky puppy	a hungry kitten
a sunny jungle	sixty skinny men
an empty bottle	hundreds of ugly rats
a tennis racket	a stretchy rubber band
a sandy pebble	a stick of bubble gum
a waxy candle	seven running joggers
a wet paddle	your uncle's sunglasses
a rocky river	a winning raffle ticket
a little thimble	twenty sloppy bathtubs
a messy closet	a dish of blackberry jelly
an empty bucket	seventy snapping lobsters

Tricky Steps to Save a Skinny Little Kitty

NAME _____   DATE _____

This little kitty is lost and very hungry. She needs **your** help! Start at the bottom of the steps and climb up quickly! Find the word that will complete each sentence along the way. You must fill in every blank with the right word.

If something is funny, you will _____.
(wiggle, giggle, sizzle)

If it is sunny, it can be very _____.
(foggy, nasty, hot)

If my uncle is a jolly man, he must be _____.
(happy, bossy, fussy)

If a rocky path is wet and muddy, it can be very _____. (slippery, hilly)

If a puppy is frisky, he is _____.
(grumpy, peppy, rusty)

If Betty is happy, she must be _____.
(sad, upset, glad)

If an apple is very fresh, it will be _____.
(soggy, crispy, rotten)

If you are my best pal, you are my _____.
(body, hobby, buddy)

If Andy is angry, he is _____.
(dizzy, mad, happy)

If your tummy is empty. you must be _____.
(hungry, ugly, dusty)

If a man is very thin, he is _____.
(skinny, fat, silly)

A peppermint candy can be _____.
(picky, muddy, sticky)

39

A Special Spelling Secret

When a word **ends** with a **consonant** and a **y**, we must change the y to an i before we add __es, __er, or __est.

puppy

This is a word that ends with a consonant and a y. If we want to make **puppy** a plural word, we must add an __**es**.

puppies

This is a plural word: **puppies**. We must change a **y** to an **i** <u>before</u> we add the __es.

| puppy
puppies | cherry
cherries | buddy
buddies | penny
pennies |

happy

This is a word that ends with a consonant and a y. We must change the **y** to an **i** before we add __er or __est.

happier

happiest

| funny
funnier
funniest | muddy
muddier
muddiest | hungry
hungrier
hungriest |

40

Spelling Words on Nutty Buddies

NAME _____ DATE _____

On every Nutty Buddy ice-cream cone below, you will see 2 pictures. One of the pictures has already been named. You must write the words that name the pictures on the ice cream! All your words will be plural. All your words will end with __ies.

puppy

penny

seventy

cherry

mommy

bunny

twenty

buggy

blackberry

Spelling Words for Shaggy Puppies

NAME _____ DATE _____

Every puppy below is holding 1 word and 2 word endings. Add each of the endings to the word. Spell 2 new words! Write your words on the blanks. Then read all your words to your teacher!

Dogtown's Peppermint Raffle

Win a bundle of peppermints from Uncle Randy's Candy Pantry!

YOU WILL NEED: 2 players
a gameboard (on page 44)
36 game cards (on pages 45 and 46)
2 gameboard markers

1. Look at the gameboard. Two players will race down the path of peppermints to win a big bundle of candies from Uncle Randy's Candy Pantry!

2. Look at the game cards. These will be your raffle tickets. Each card has a question on it. Cut out all the cards. Put them in a pile face down on the gameboard.

3. Place your game markers on the START space.

4. **Player # 1:** Draw a raffle ticket. Read the question out loud and answer it. Player #2 will check you. If the answer to your question is "YES," COUNT THE CANDIES on the card and jump ahead that many peppermints. If the answer to your question is "NO," DO NOT count the candies on the card. Instead, you will STAY where you are until your next turn. **Player # 2:** Now you do the same.

5. Take turns drawing, reading, and answering questions, one at a time. The first player to reach Uncle Randy's Candy Pantry will WIN the Dogtown Peppermint Raffle!

Dogtown's Peppermint Raffle
Win a bundle of peppermints from Uncle Randy's Candy Pantry!

START HERE

Raffle Tickets

Uncle Randy's Candy Pantry

Bundles of Peppermints for Raffle Winners!!

Dogtown's Peppermint Raffle

(Game Cards)

Raffle Tickets ♪

Will a bunny have freckles on her ankles?	Can an ant gobble up fifty apples in six seconds?	Can a bathtub be filled with sudsy bubbles?
Can one mask be funnier than another one?	Can peppermint candies be sticky?	Can you put a thimble on your middle finger?
Will fifty big doll buggies fit into a picnic basket?	Can a hungry bunny nibble on grass?	Will you chuckle if you think something is funny?
Can shoppers be picky?	Will butter melt and sizzle in a hot skillet?	Can a runner quickly tackle a kicker?
Can you toss a sandy pebble into a river?	Will twenty little cherries fit into a bucket?	Will puppies be friskier than cattle?
Can you get hungry for a yummy snack?	Will a rotten apple be crispy?	Can you fill an empty bottle with sand?

Dogtown's Peppermint Raffle

(Game Cards)

Raffle Tickets

Can you scramble an egg in a hot skillet?	Can you wiggle your fingers?	Can sixty very ugly rats buckle your belt?
Can a sandwich have blackberry jelly on it?	Can seventy grumpy mummies swing in a jungle?	Can a dentist be skinnier than his little brother?
Can a pretty pink candle flicker?	Can a stick of bubble gum giggle?	Could a box of crispy crackers be in a kitchen pantry?
Can a silly fox fix a scrambled egg?	Do crabs and clams have shells on their bodies?	Can an uncle get angry?
Can you slip six pennies into a piggy bank?	Can you sit on an empty saddle?	Can you put together a very simple puzzle?
Will a kettle have a handle on it?	Can you tickle a puppy?	Can you nibble on a crunchy dill pickle?

R-Controlled Vowels

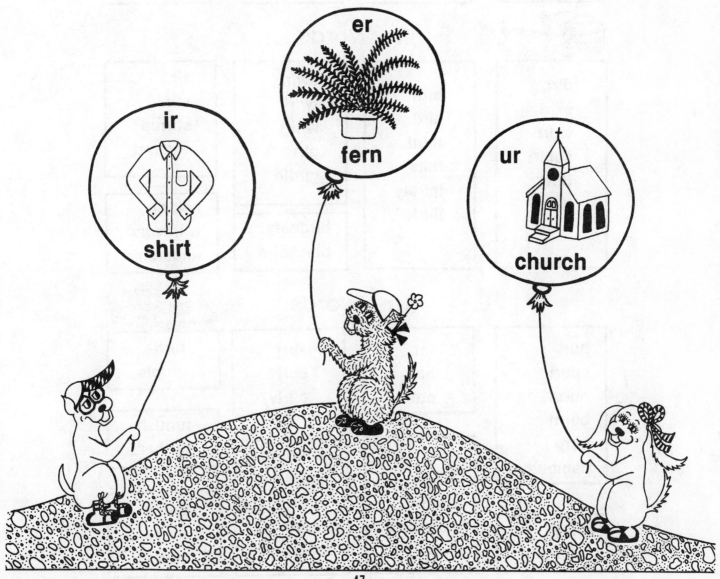

Words to Read and Spell

er Words

her	servant	lantern	interest
verb	sermon	cavern	interesting
jerk	person	tavern	interrupt
perk	perfect	pattern	
clerk	perhaps	western	
fern	permanent	modern	were
stern			nerve
term			serve
perch	thermometer	camera	swerve
		shepherd	verse

ir Words

dirt	birth	swirl	sir
skirt	bird	twirl	stir
shirt	third	whirl	stirrup
squirt	thirst	girl	squirrel
flirt	thirsty	girdle	
first	thirty		aspirin
firm		birdbath	whirlwind
		blackbird	undershirt

ur Words

hurt	fur	surf	turtle
spurt	blur	curl	purple
burst	purr	curly	
burnt			furnish
burp	urn	sunburn	further
hamburger	burn	murder	
	turn	surrender	purse
curb	churn	hurry	nurse
disturb	church	nursery	curve

48

Rhyming Words on Turtles and Birds

NAME _____ DATE _____

🐾 On every turtle and bird below, you will see a word ending and a group of letters. Add each of the letters to the word ending and spell rhyming words! Write your words on the blanks. Then read all your words to your teacher.

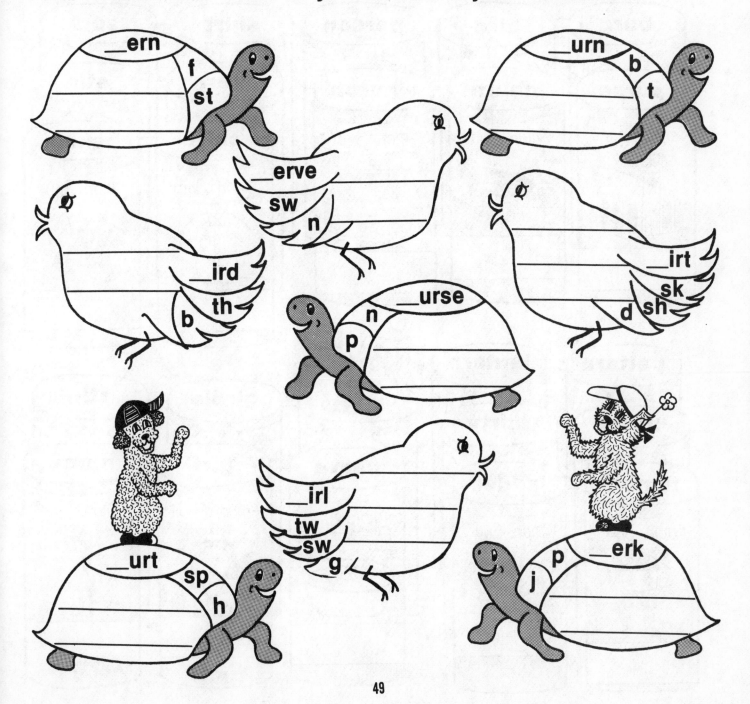

WIN A SIX-PACK OF LEMON SQUIRT!

NAME _____   DATE _____

🐾 **If you can find and write the word that names every picture below, you will win a six-pack of Lemon Squirt! Write all your words on the cans.**

burp | bird | person | shirt | surf

purse | churn | church | stern | stir

skirt | skip

pattern | lantern

turtle | thirty | girdle | stir

tumble | ladder | nerve | girl | nurse

50

Hungry? Thirsty? Hurry to Herbert's Better Burger!

NAME _____ DATE _____

Come join the dogs for hamburgers and drinks at Herbert's Better Burger! To get to the hamburger stand, you must follow the path of sentences. Find and write the word that will complete each sentence. If you are hungry and thirsty, Herbert is ready to serve you!

When a cat is happy, he will _____.
(burp, purr, sniffle)

A helper in a hospital can be a _____.
(nurse, nerve, nest)

A sister is a _____.
(brother, girl)

A dog can have long curly _____.
(fingers, fur, first)

You must put film into a _____.
(church, camera)

When a bird sings, he _____.
(burps, chirps, sobs)

If a truck flashes its blinker, it is _____.
(burning, turning)

If you chug or guzzle a drink, you must be very _____.
(dirty, dizzy, thirsty)

If you burn your little finger, it will _____.
(hurt, burst, twirl)

If a man is running, he must be in a _____.
(church, hurry, girdle)

A thick shell will cover the body of a _____.
(squirrel, bird, turtle)

Herbert's Better Burger

51

LET'S TALK ABOUT
the Sounds of **or** and **ar**

40

or

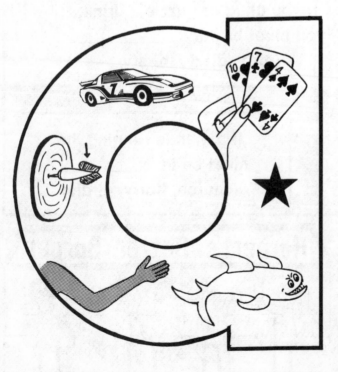

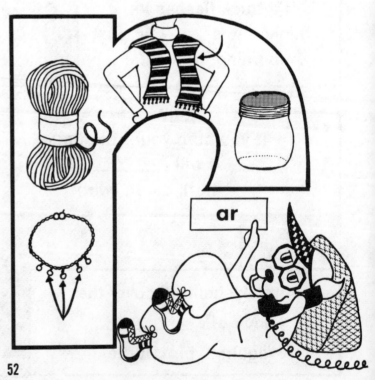

ar

52

Words to Read and Spell

or Words

or for lord	fort sort port short sport support comfort important	born corn horn torn worn thorn popcorn stubborn	north forth forty forest forget forgot forever florist	organ order corner border boring morning story history

dorm storm form inform perform platform			

cork fork pork stork	actor tractor

torch porch		horse

DOGGONE EXCEPTIONS

word worm world	worth worse worst

ar Words

bar car far tar jar par scar star darling	yard card hard hardy tardy	arm farm harm charm alarm army	art dart cart tart part smart start chart party	gargle marble

	carve starve

mustard custard buzzard lizard wizard	bark dark lark mark park shark spark	artist article

tarnish target market carpet carport carton carpenter	arc arch march starch scarf	barn yarn	farther barber bartender kindergarten

		birthmark starfish	

DOGGONE EXCEPTIONS

war wart	warn warm

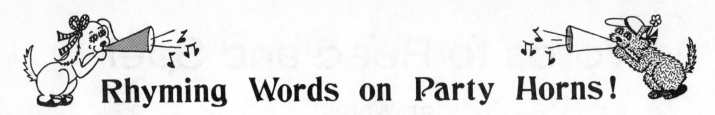

Rhyming Words on Party Horns!

NAME _____ DATE _____

On every party horn below, you will see a word ending and a group of letters. Add each of the letters to the word ending and spell rhyming words! Write your words on the blanks. Read all your words to your teacher.

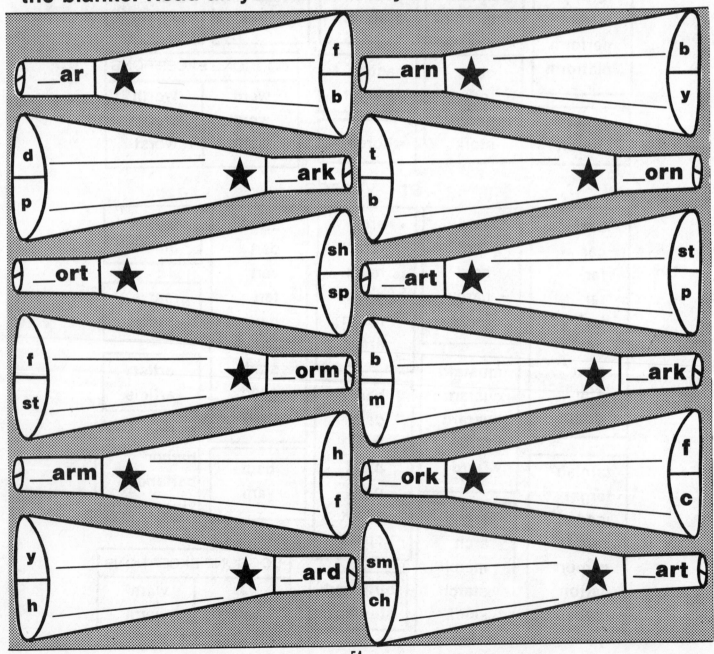

Lucky Cards for Terrific Spellers!

If you can spell the word that names each picture below, you will turn an ordinary card into a lucky one! Circle the correct sound for every picture. Then write your words on the blanks.

or / ar	ir / ar	or / ur	ar / ur	ir / ar

    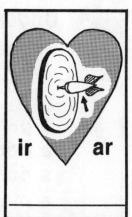

ir / or	er / ar	ir / or	ar / ir	er / or

  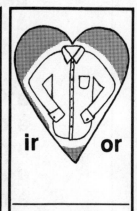  

ar / ur	or / ar	er / or	ar / or	ur / or

CATEGORIES

NAME _____ DATE _____

 Underline all the things below that you can pick up with your hands.

a park	a little bird
a cork	a party horn
a dart	a sunny porch
a marble	a burning torch
a turtle	an alarm clock
a forest	a little lizard
a purse	a farmer's barn
a girdle	a hard pebble
a church	a foggy morning
a camera	a deck of cards
a lantern	a popcorn popper
a sunburn	a stubborn horse
a starfish	a marching army
a yardstick	a jar of mustard
a hamburger	sixty barking dogs
a corncob	forty skinny nurses
a sharp fork	a carton of eggs
a dark storm	twenty short girls
a dirty shirt	thirty thirsty pigs
a purple skirt	a bottle of aspirin
a purring cat	fifty burping buzzards

⋆★ Blast Off to the Stars!

YOU WILL NEED:
- 2 astronauts
- a gameboard (on page 58)
- 36 game cards (on page 59 and 60)
- 2 gameboard markers

Dear Teacher: Please provide a Medal of Honor for the astronaut that wins this game. Thanks!

1. Look at the gameboard. Two astronauts will join the dogs for a trip through a galaxy of stars. They will blast off in the space shuttle. Then they will follow the path of stars to the Space Station. Each big star is one space on the gameboard.

2. Look at the game cards. Each card has a question on it. Cut out all the cards. Put them in a pile face down.

3. Place your markers on the START space.

4. **Astronaut # 1:** Draw a game card. Read the question out loud and answer it. Astronaut #2 will check you. If the answer to your question is "YES," COUNT THE STARS on your card and hurry **forward** that many spaces. If the answer to your question is "NO," you must COUNT THE STARS on the card and dart **backwards** that many spaces. **Astronaut #2:** Now you do the same.

5. Take turns drawing, reading and answering questions, one at a time. The first astronaut to reach the Space Station will win a Medal of Honor!

Blast Off to the Stars!

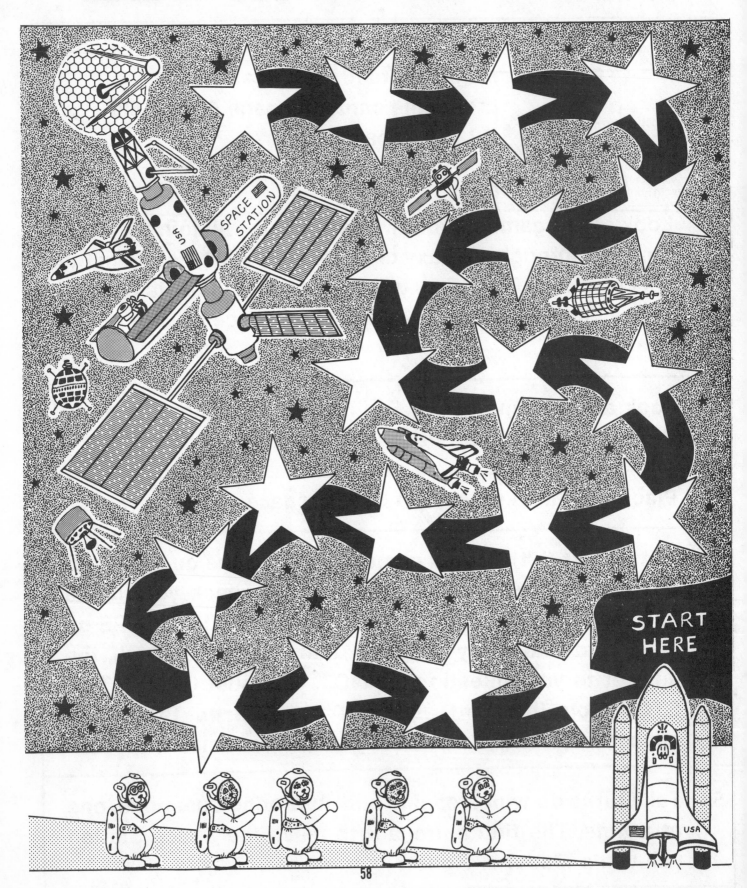

☆ Blast Off to the Stars!
(Game Cards)

Can a fat squirrel shop for a carton of eggs? ★★	Can a black horse shuffle a deck of cards? ★★	Can an artist sketch a farmer's barn? ★★★
Can a barber trim a shaggy dog's fur? ★★	Can a snack bar serve hamburgers and drinks? ★★★	Will butter melt in a hot popcorn popper? ★★
Can thunder crash during a wet and windy storm? ★★★	Can six puppies be born on a sunny morning? ★ ★	Can a nurse have a thermometer in her skirt pocket? ★★★
Can a horse nap in a barn? ★	Can a man have a party in his front yard? ★★	Can a frisky dog jerk on the arm of your shirt? ★★★
Can a mom park her car next to a curb? ★★	Can a thorny branch cut your finger? ★	Can an uncle serve pork ribs at his dinner party? ★★★
Will napkins, forks and a jar of mustard fit into a picnic basket? ★★	Can a barking turtle gobble up a wet carpet? ★★	After you chug a big fizzy drink, can you burp? ★★

☆Blast Off to the Stars!
(Game Cards)

Can a girl's skirt get dirty? ★★	Will a mom serve a purple girdle for lunch? ★★	If you must not disturb a person, will you whisper? ★★★
If you burn your arm, will it hurt? ★★	Can a short fat man swim in a little birdbath? ★	Can a nurse give an aspirin to a sick person? ★★★
If a turtle is happy, will he purr? ★	If a farmer has lots of land and crops, will he have a tractor? ★★	Can an army of ants pick up a fork and stir a muffin batter? ★★
Will an alarm clock ring? ★	Can a person get hungry and thirsty? ★★	Will a bird have long curly fur? ★★
Can a history class be interesting? ★★	Can the tips of a fork be sharp? ★★	Can a bundle of yarn bark? ★
Can a story be boring? ★	Can a car turn left at a corner? ★★	Can a little camera fit into a purse? ★★

LET'S TALK ABOUT
the Sound of Long A /ā/

The **long a** sound says **/ā/**.

LET'S TALK ABOUT
the Sound of Long E /ē/

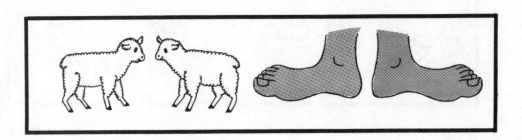

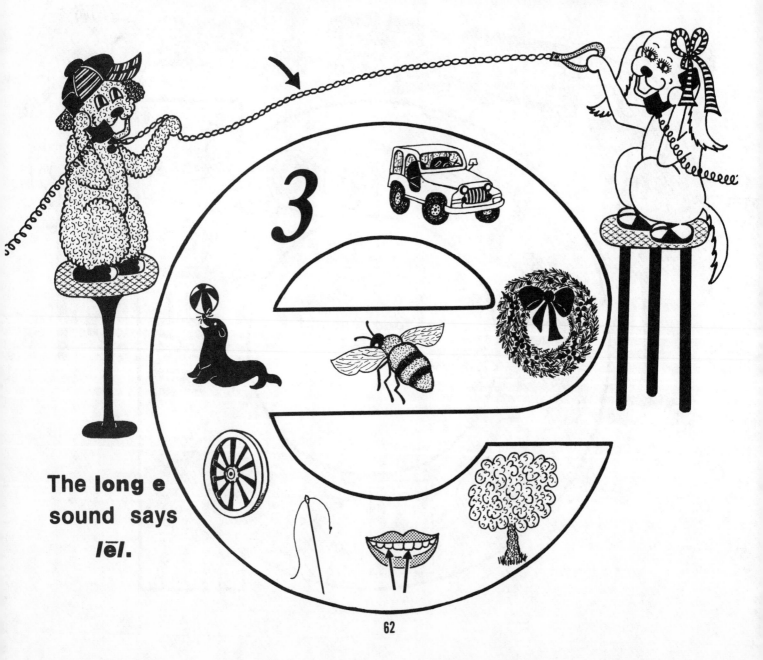

3

The long e sound says /ē/.

LET'S TALK ABOUT
the Sound of Long I /Ī/

The long i sound says /ī/.

LET'S TALK ABOUT
the Sound of Long O /ō/

The **long o** sound says
/ō/.

LET'S TALK ABOUT
the Sound of Long U /ū/

SPARKLE
TOOTH PASTE
MINT FLAVOR

tube

SKY ROCKET

The **long u** sound says /ū/.

row, row your boat gently down the stream.

65

Stop for the Right Vowel Sound!

STOP

NAME _____

DATE _____

Can you STOP for the
right vowel sound?

Every stop sign below has a picture on it. The name of
each picture will have a long or a short vowel sound. Circle
the **right** vowel sound for every picture.

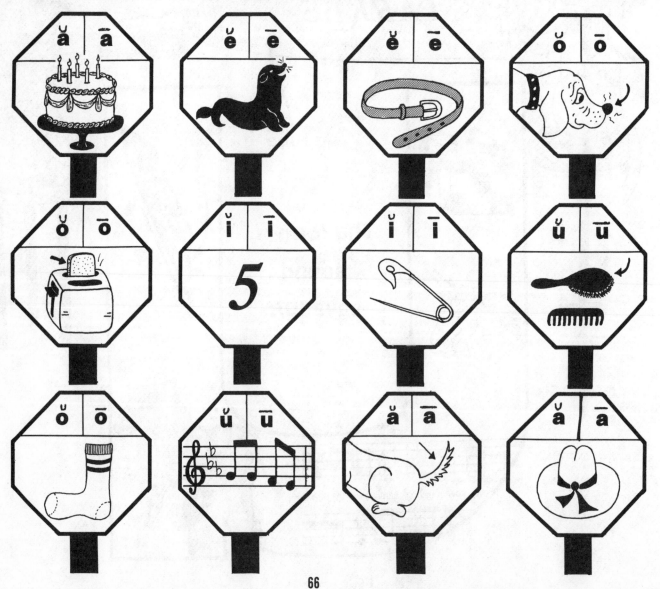

Stop for the Right Vowel Sound!

NAME _____

DATE _____

Can you STOP for the **right** vowel sound?

Every stop sign below has a picture on it. The name of each picture will have a short or a long vowel sound. Circle the **right** vowel sound for every picture.

67

A Special Spelling Secret

A silent **e** at the **end** of a one-syllable word can perform magic!

ă	ĕ	ĭ	ŏ	ŭ
mad	pet	slid	hop	cut

Here we have 5 one-syllable words.
Each word has a **short** vowel sound.

If we put an **e** on the **end** of each word
above, the vowel sounds will change!

ā	ē	ī	ō	ū
made	Pete	slide	hope	cute

The e at the end of each word above is silent.
All of our new words have long vowel sounds.

 **When a one-syllable word ends with a silent e,
it will almost always have a long vowel sound.**

Words to Read and Spell

can	bit	hop
cane	bite	hope
Jan	kit	rob
Jane	kite	robe
man	quit	not
mane	quite	note
mad	win	rod
made	wine	rode
fad	shin	
fade	shine	
		cut
cap	rip	cute
cape	ripe	
		tub
tap	grip	tube
tape	gripe	
past	hid	pet
paste	hide	Pete
bath	slid	
bathe	slide	

Step Up and Slide!

NAME _____ DATE _____

🐾 Circle the word that will name each picture on the slides!

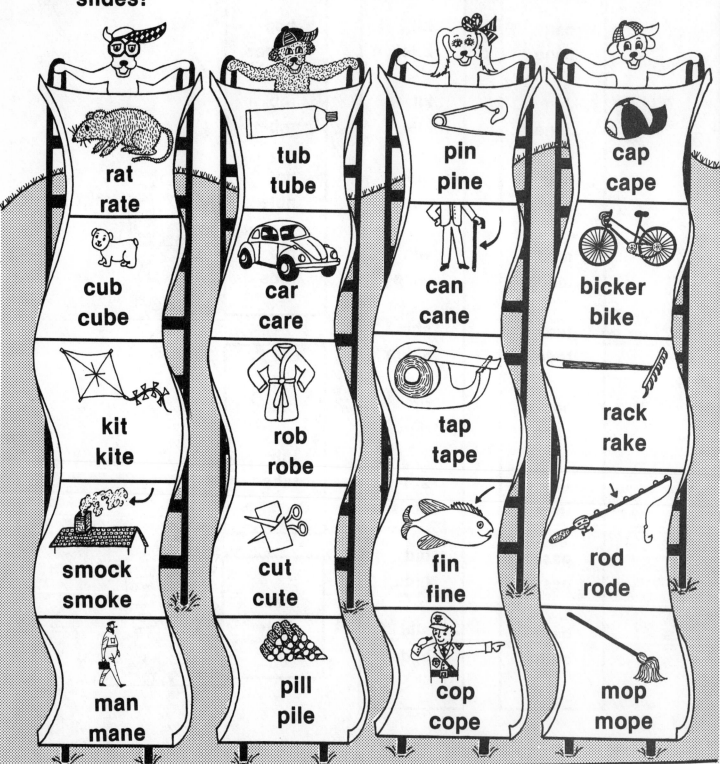

rat / rate	tub / tube	pin / pine	cap / cape
cub / cube	car / care	can / cane	bicker / bike
kit / kite	rob / robe	tap / tape	rack / rake
smock / smoke	cut / cute	fin / fine	rod / rode
man / mane	pill / pile	cop / cope	mop / mope

Long Vowel Sounds

Words that End with a "Magic" e

Words to Read and Spell

Long A /ā/ Words

cane	fade	ape	daze	pale
lane	wade	cape	haze	sale
mane	made	tape	gaze	tale
pane				male
	blade	drape	blaze	
plane	shade	grape	glaze	
crane	trade	scrape	graze	scale
insane	spade	shape	craze	stale
	invade	escape	amaze	whale

ā

came	cave	bake	ate
fame	gave	cake	date
name	pave	fake	hate
same	wave	lake	late
tame	save	make	rate
lame	rave	rake	gate
game		take	
	slave	wake	plate
blame	shave		skate
flame	brave	flake	grate
frame	crave	brake	state
shame	grave	snake	
		awake	
		mistake	

base	safe
case	unsafe
vase	
chase	

taste
waste
baste
haste
paste

bathe

pavement
statement
basement

lemonade
blockade
decorate

DOGGONE EXCEPTIONS	
have	are

72

Escape on a Rhyming Whale!

NAME _____ DATE _____

On every whale below, you will see a word ending and a group of letters. Add the word ending to each of the letters and spell rhyming words! Write your words on the blanks. Read all your words to your teacher!

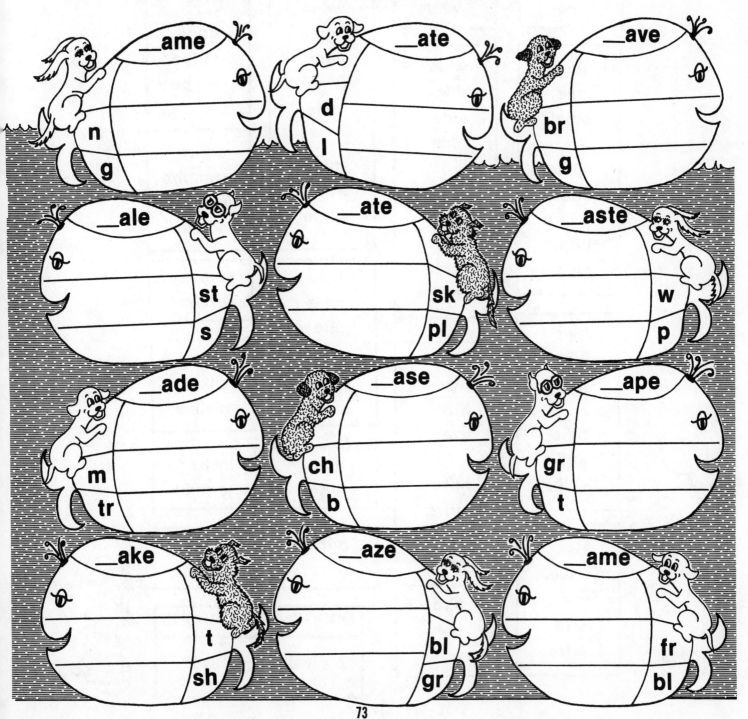

73

Words to Read and Spell

Long I /ī/ Words

die
lie
tie
pie

bite
kite
quite
white

dine
fine
line
wine
mine
nine
vine
pine

shine
whine
spine

pipe
ripe
wipe

gripe
stripe
swipe

dime
lime
time

slime
crime
grime
prime
chime

wide
ride
side
hide

glide
slide
bride
pride
inside

entire
vampire
umpire
admire

file
mile
pile

while
smile

surprise
survive

bike
hike
like

trike
strike
spike

dive
five
hive
live

drive
strive
thrive

alive
alike
dislike

life
wife

invite
termite

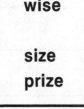

rise
wise

size
prize

hire
tire
wire

bribe
tribe

baptize
advertise

DOGGONE EXCEPTIONS	
give	live

74

STARS AND RHYMING STRIPES!

NAME _____ DATE _____

Inside each star on the flags, you will see a letter. On every flag stand, you will see a word ending. Add the ending to each of the letters and spell rhyming words! Write your words across the white stripes. Read all your words to your teacher.

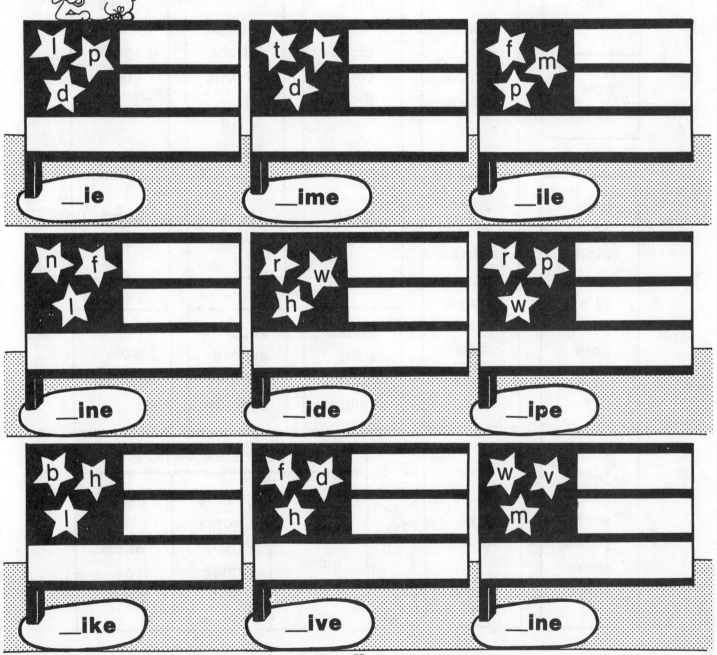

75

Words to Read and Spell

Long O /ō/ Words

hoe	hope	dose	bone	joke
toe	cope	hose	cone	poke
	lope	pose	tone	woke
Joe	dope	nose	zone	
woe	mope	rose		broke
	rope		stone	smoke
		close	shone	spoke
note	slope	chose	throne	choke
quote	scope	those		

bore	cove	code	doze	dome
core	dove	rode	froze	home
more	wove			
sore				
tore	drove	awoke	suppose	
wore	stove	alone	expose	insole
pore	clove	adore	explore	envelope
		ignore	explode	

store		
spore	hole	
score	mole	/ō/
snore	pole	
swore	sole	
chore		
shore	stole	

DOGGONE EXCEPTIONS		
love	come	gone
dove	some	
glove	none	whose
shove	done	lose
	one	shoe

76

Rhyming Notes in Envelopes

NAME _____ DATE _____

Inside every envelope below, you will see a piece of paper. It has a word ending and a list of letters on it. Add the ending to each of the letters and spell rhyming words! Write your words on the lines. Then read all your rhyming notes to your teacher!

__ole

h
m
p

__ose

th
n
cl

__ope

r
sl
h

__oke

br
ch
j
sm

__ore

m
s
ch
sn
st
sc

__one

b
st
c
z

Words to Read and Spell

Long E /ē/ Words

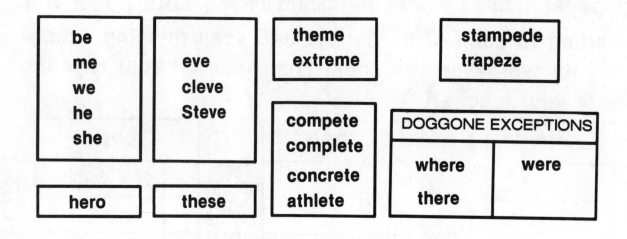

be me we he she	eve cleve Steve

theme extreme

stampede trapeze

hero	these

compete complete concrete athlete

DOGGONE EXCEPTIONS	
where there	were

_UE and _U_E /ū/, /yoo/, and /oo/ Words

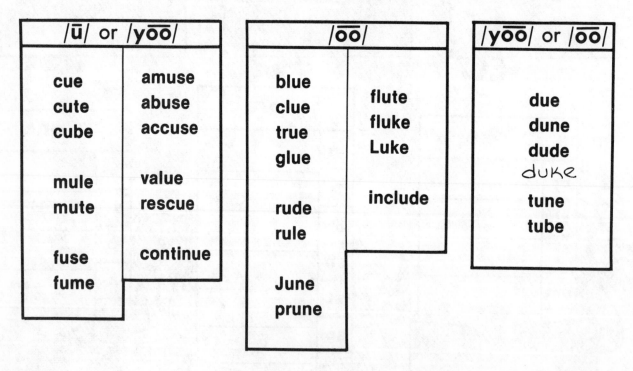

/ū/ or /yoo/

cue cute cube	amuse abuse accuse
mule mute	value rescue
fuse fume	continue

/oo/

blue clue true glue	flute fluke Luke
rude rule	include
June prune	

/yoo/ or /oo/

due
dune
dude
duke
tune
tube

Dogtown's Rhyming Mule Stampede!

NAME _____ DATE _____

Welcome to Dogtown's Rhyming Mule Stampede!
Every dog below will show you a word ending and a group of letters. Add the ending to each of the letters and spell rhyming words. Write your words on the mules. Then read all your words to your teacher.

__ue

tr	bl

__une

t	J

__eve

cl	St

__ute

c	fl

__ube

c	t

Take a Bite of Homemade Cherry Pie!

NAME _____ DATE _____

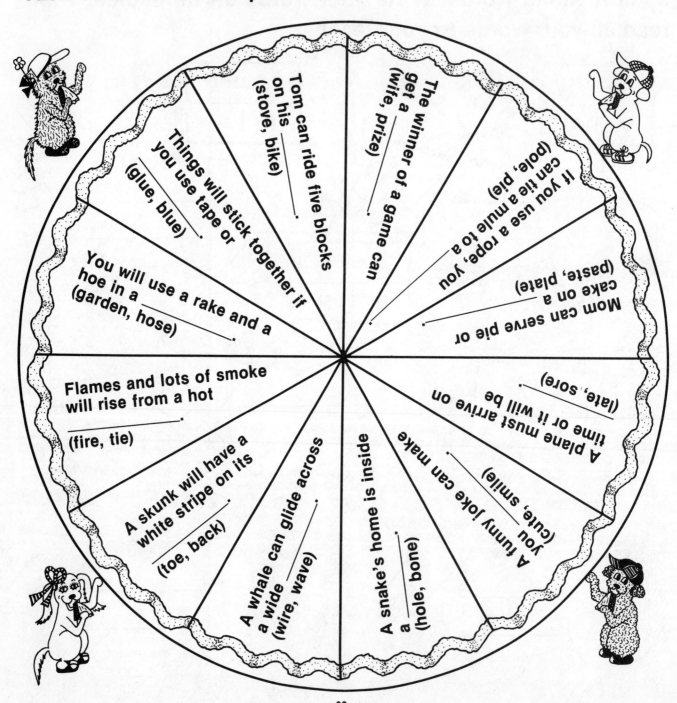

If you want a bite of homemade cherry pie, you must read carefully! Find and write the word that will complete each sentence on the pie.

The winner of a game can get a _____ .
(wife, prize)

Tom can ride five blocks on his _____ .
(stove, bike)

Things will stick together if you use tape or _____ .
(glue, blue)

You will use a rake and a hoe in a _____ .
(garden, hose)

Flames and lots of smoke will rise from a hot _____ .
(fire, tie)

A skunk will have a white stripe on its _____ .
(toe, back)

A whale can glide across a wide _____ .
(wire, wave)

A snake's home is inside a _____ .
(hole, bone)

A funny joke can make you _____ .
(cute, smile)

A plane must arrive on time or it will be _____ .
(late, sore)

Mom can serve pie or cake on a _____ .
(paste, plate)

If you use a rope, you can tie a mule to a _____ .
(pole, pie)

80

A Five-Mile Ride to Lots of Shade and Lemonade!

NAME _____   DATE _____

🐾 It is a hot sunny day in June. So come join the dogs for a long bike ride! You will ride five miles. Then you will stop, rest in the shade, and have a big glass of homemade lemonade! As you ride down the bike path, you must write the word that will name each picture.

A Safe Ride to Shore on an Inner Tube !

WELCOME TO DOGTOWN LAKE!
Hop on an inner tube and join the
dogs for a wet race to shore!

YOU WILL NEED: a gameboard (on page 83)
45 game cards (on page 84)
1 announcer
5 inner tube racers

The first inner tube racer to write <u>nine</u> words on a lane ... <u>WINS</u> !

1. **Look at the gameboard. Each inner tube racer will splash down the lake with one of the dogs! Pick a racing lane and remember its vowel sound.**

2. **Look at the game cards. All the words have long vowel sounds. Each word ends with a "magic" e. Cut out all the cards. Put them in a pile face down.**

3. **Announcer: Draw a game card. Read the word to the inner tube racers. Don't let them see the word! Inner Tube Racers: Listen to the vowel sound of the word. The racer whose lane has that vowel sound will write the word on the first space of his/her lane.**

4. **Announcer: Keep drawing and reading word cards one at a time. Give the inner tube racers time to write each word. Inner Tube Racers: Keep splashing down Dogtown Lake. Write only words that have the vowel sound of your racing lane. Get to shore safely!**

A Safe Ride to Shore on an Inner Tube!

A Safe Ride to Shore on an Inner Tube !

(Game Cards)

shave	compete	time	cute	note
more	shine	late	these	mule
cube	we	smoke	wire	bake
drive	tune	he	home	life
theme	save	glue	game	be
grape	hope	smile	use	joke
fuse	dive	state	me	blue
tube	paste	note	inside	take
wide	snore	complete	close	she

Compound Words

2 whole words put together
and spelled as 1 big word

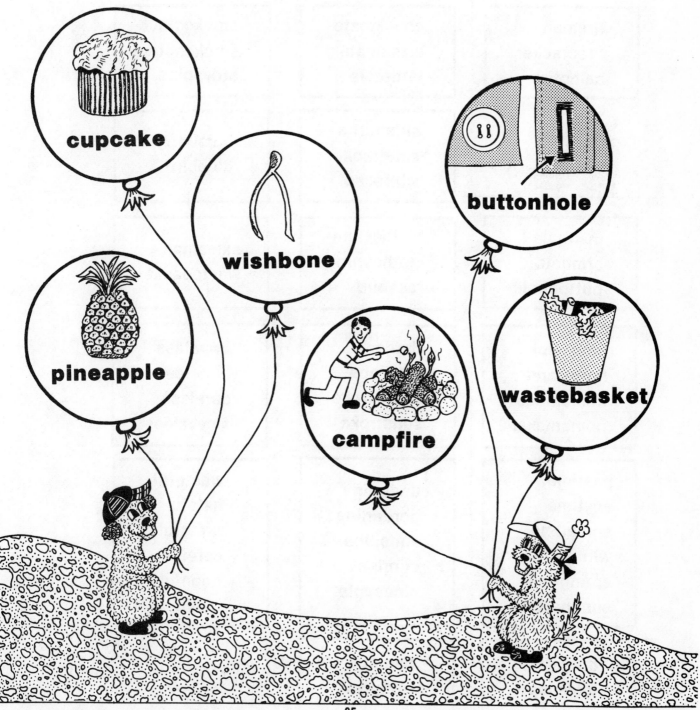

cupcake

wishbone

buttonhole

pineapple

campfire

wastebasket

Words to Read and Spell

cupcake
pancake
handshake
nickname

backbone
wishbone
limestone
sandstone

necktie
potpie
frostbite

fireman
firecracker
campfire

checkmate
classmate
tattletale

smokestack
smokehouse
stovepipe

sideburns
sidetrack
whitecap

blueberry
bluebird

manhole
armhole
buttonhole

clothesline
clothespin
rosebud

salesman
wastebasket

homesick
homeland
homemade
homemaker

tiptoe
bathrobe
backstroke
sunstroke

hopeless
boneless
careless
sleeveless

pastime
anytime
sometime
wintertime
springtime
summertime

underline
borderline
sunshine
sunrise
pineapple

wasteful
hateful
grateful
careful
hopeful
useful

drugstore
telescope

bagpipe
turnpike

TEE OFF FOR A HOLE IN ONE!

DOGTOWN COUNTRY CLUB

Join the dogs for nine holes of golf! Hit the ball on every tee box and follow it down the fairway. You must add together the 2 words on each fairway. Then write a compound word on the green! When you finish, read all the words you wrote to your teacher. For every word you spell and read correctly, you will score a hole in one!

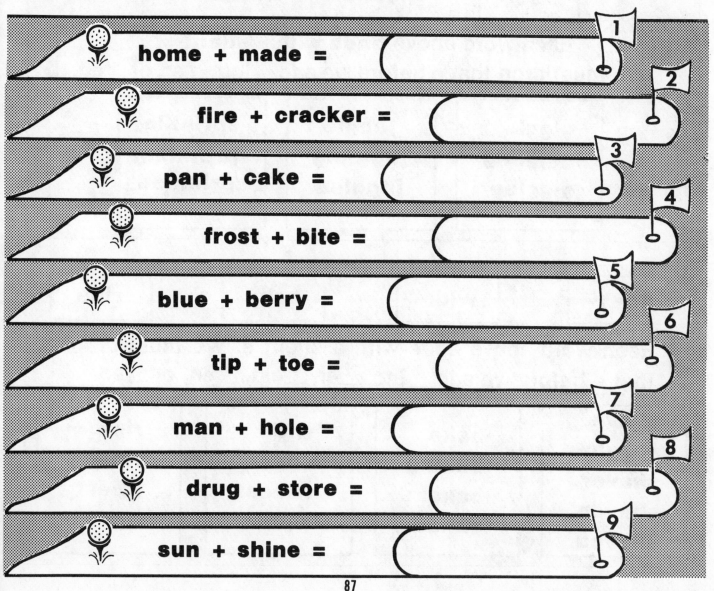

home + made =

fire + cracker =

pan + cake =

frost + bite =

blue + berry =

tip + toe =

man + hole =

drug + store =

sun + shine =

A Special Spelling Secret

SPELL CAREFULLY when you add __ing, __er, __est, __en and __ed to words that **end** with a **silent e.**

giggle	juggle	sprinkle

Each word above ends with a silent e.
We must drop that **e** before we add __ing, __er, or __ed.

giggle	juggle	sprinkle
giggling	juggling	sprinkling
giggled	juggled	sprinkled

shave	wide	bake	ripe

Each word above ends with a silent e. We must drop that e before we add __ing, __er, __est, __en, or __ed.

shave	bake	wide	ripe
shaving	baking	wider	riper
shaver	baker	widest	ripest
shaven	baked	widen	ripen
shaved			

Untangling Sprinkler Hoses

On every hose below, you will see a word and an ending. Add them together, spell a new word, and you will untangle the sprinkler hoses! Write your words on the blank spaces inside the sprinklers.

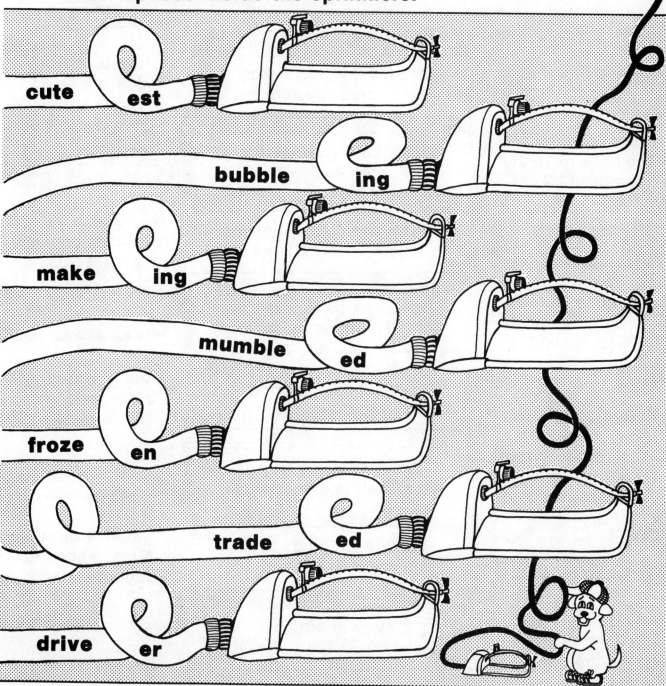

cute + est

bubble + ing

make + ing

mumble + ed

froze + en

trade + ed

drive + er

Pipe Puzzlers

🐾 Can you answer a pipe puzzler? First, read the sentence on the pipe stem. Then find a sentence on the pipe bowl that means the same thing and underline it!

Joe makes pies, cakes, and homemade cookies.

Joe is a biker.
Joe is a baker.
Joe is a joker.

The boss fired Jeff.
The boss hired Jeff.
The boss bit Jeff.

The boss gave Jeff a part-time job.

We cannot stop giggling when Randy tells jokes.

He makes us tired.
He makes us smile.
He makes us lie.

Bob is shining.
Bob is griping.
Bob is sharing.

Bob gave his cookies to five of his pals.

Jill is mixing up a deck of cards.

Jill is shuffling.
Jill is waking up.
Jill is shaving.

The vase is frozen.
The vase is blue.
The vase is broken.

The glass vase fell off the shelf and shattered.

Mom is taking us to the store in her car.

Mom is diving.
Mom is snoring.
Mom is driving.

It is braking.
It is melting.
It is blazing.

A stick of butter is sizzling in the skillet.

90

Vowel Digraphs

2 Vowels Sitting Side by Side

The first vowel does the talking.
The second vowel is silent.

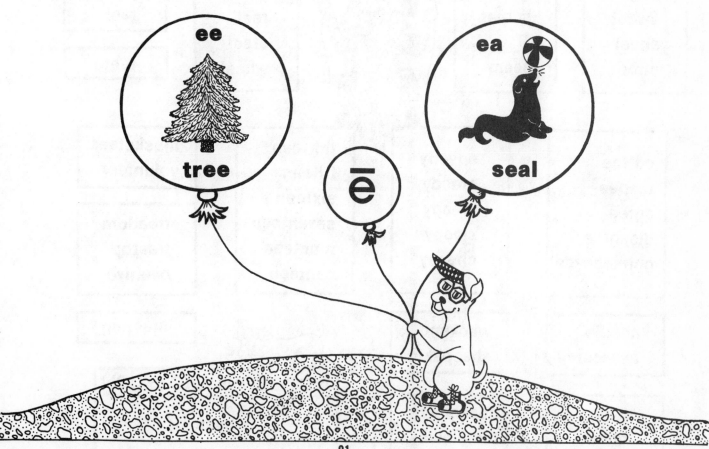

Words to Read and Spell

ee/ē/Words

bee	deed	freeze	week	beep
fee	feed	breeze	peek	deep
see	need	sneeze	seek	keep
wee	seed	wheeze	creek	peep
tee	weed	squeeze	cheek	jeep
free	bleed			weep
tree	greed	cheese	speech	creep
three	speed	geese	screch	sleep
				steep
				sweep
				sheep

feet	seen	eel	
beet	teen	feel	
meet	queen	heel	beef
sleet	green	peel	reef
sweet	screen	reel	
sheet		steel	teeth
street	seem	wheel	

ee   ē

coffee	speedy	thirteen	musketeer
teepee	greedy	fifteen	volunteer
agree	creepy	sixteen	
disagree	sleepy	seventeen	freedom
chimpanzee	cheesy	nineteen	treetop
		canteen	beehive

needle	weekend	meeting
tweezers	sheepskin	

asleep	nosebleed
indeed	tumbleweed

A DOGGONE EXCEPTION

been

Words to Read and Spell

ea /ē/ Words

pea
sea
tea
flea

beak
leak
peak
weak

bean
mean
lean
clean

deal
meal
real
seal
steal

peach
reach
beach
teach
preach

ea

ē

eat
beat
feat
heat
meat
neat
seat
treat
cheat
wheat
pleat

beam
seam
team
dream
gleam
cream
steam
stream
scream

east
beast
feast
yeast

leave
heave
weave

lead
read
bead

ease
please
tease

leap
cheap

grease
crease

teacup
teapot
peanut
peacock
seaweed
seashell
seashore
seasick

realize
reason
season
weasel

disease
displease
disappear

easy
greasy
creamy
really

beanbag
teammate
seamstress
weakness
treatment

beaver
leader
teacher
bleachers
preacher
eastern
Easter

meantime
meanwhile

unreal
underneath
anteater

Sweeping Words into Dustpans

NAME _____ DATE _____

Help the dogs finish their sweeping chores! On every broom below, you will see a word ending. On the bits of trash, you will see letters. Add the ending to each of the letters and spell rhyming words. Write your words inside the dustpans. Read all your words to your teacher!

94

Sweeten a Teapot with Rhyming Words!

NAME _____   DATE _____

🐾 Help the dogs sweeten a big pot of tea! On each Sweet 'n Easy sugar packet, you will see a word ending. On the spout of every teapot, you will see a list of letters. Add the ending to each of the letters and spell rhyming words.

95

One...Two...Three... Say "Cheese!"

NAME _____ **DATE** _____

What kinds of pictures are the dogs taking? You can tell us! Find and write the word that will name every picture on the camera lenses.

bee
feet
heel
tree
teeth
geese
sheep
three
wheel
needle
fifteen
sixteen

$$ Dogtown's Beanbag Sweepstakes $$

NAME _____ DATE _____

You have just picked the winning ticket for Dogtown's Beanbag Sweepstakes! If you can find and write the word that will name every picture on the beanbags, you will win a big chest of cash!

Beanbag
Sweepstakes
$$ Ticket $

beads
peas
seal
leaf
beak
team
beans
read
steam
beach
dream
beaver
peach
peanut

309751

Meet the Team for a Feast!

NAME _____ DATE _____

The Dogtown soccer team has invited you to a grand end-of-the-season feast! Lots of fun and plenty to eat! You must speed down Sixteenth Street and meet the dogs at the park. Find and write the word that will complete each sentence along the way!

Sixteenth Street

A seal can nap on a beach and swim in the _____.
(seat, sea, seed)

Rats like to eat _____.
(cheese, cheer, cheat)

You have ten toes on your _____.
(cheek, ear, feet)

A big tree can have lots of branches and _____.
(leaks, leaves, leaps)

You can dream when you are in a deep _____.
(sweep, sweet, sleep)

The leader of your class is your _____.
(beaver, teacher, reader)

On Halloween, kids scream, "Trick or _____!"
(treat, beep, cream)

A beaver will have very sharp _____.
(tease, teams, teeth)

If you are real tired, you must be _____.
(sleepy, greasy, easy)

When you take a bath, your body gets _____.
(mean, dirty, clean)

Lunch and dinner are _____.
(peas, meals, free)

CATEGORIES

 Underline all the things below that you can put on a plate and eat.

meat	a steel pipe
ham	a ripe peach
cheese	a dill pickle
chicken	a bird's beak
tweezers	three pancakes
a meal	a bumblebee
a salad	an Easter egg
earmuffs	whipped cream
beef jerky	a soccer team
sweet peas	a sandy beach
green beans	a blueberry muffin
clean sheets	a string of beads
blue jeans	a greasy cheeseburger
cheesecake	a handful of peanuts
cherry cobbler	sixteen green grapes
pumpkin pie	nineteen wheat crackers
a mean tree	thirteen steaming teapots

Vowel Digraphs

2 Vowels Sitting Side by Side

The first vowel does the talking.
The second vowel is silent.

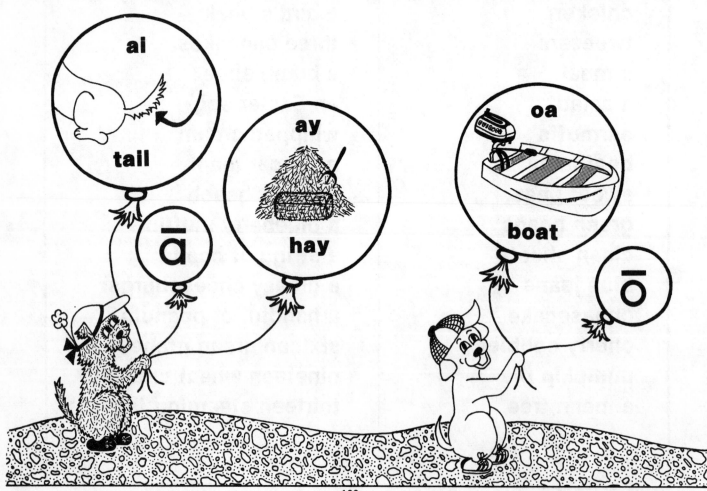

Words to Read and Spell

ai /ā/ Words

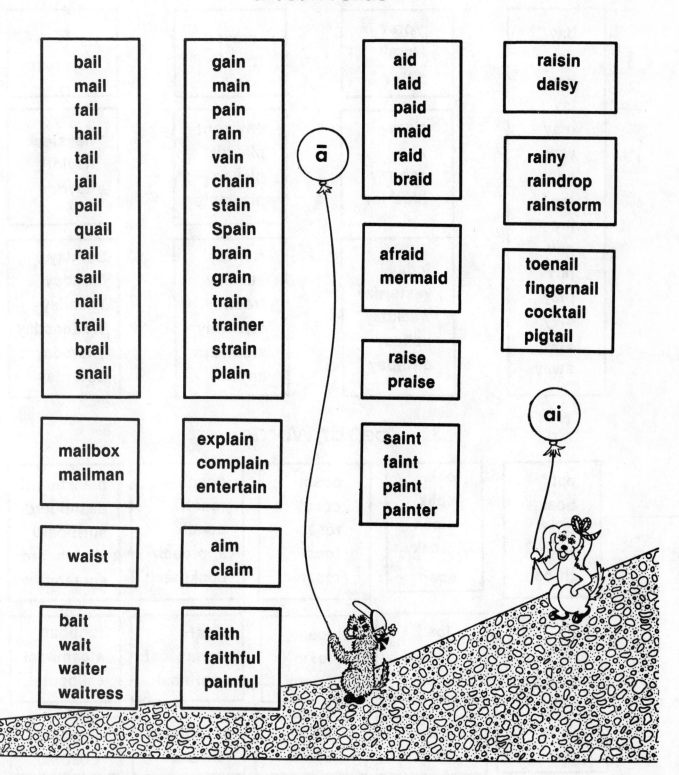

bail	gain	aid	raisin
mail	main	laid	daisy
fail	pain	paid	
hail	rain	maid	rainy
tail	vain	raid	raindrop
jail	chain	braid	rainstorm
pail	stain		
quail	Spain	afraid	toenail
rail	brain	mermaid	fingernail
sail	grain		cocktail
nail	train	raise	pigtail
trail	trainer	praise	
brail	strain		
snail	plain	saint	
		faint	
mailbox	explain	paint	
mailman	complain	painter	
	entertain		
waist	aim		
	claim		
bait	faith		
wait	faithful		
waiter	painful		
waitress			

101

Words to Read and Spell

ay /ā/ Words

bay	pray	crayon	daytime
day	gray	maybe	daydream
hay	tray		
lay			
may	away	payment	haystack
way	x-ray	playful	hayloft
say	ashtray	player	hayride
ray	blue jay	playmate	
jay			
gay	today	runway	Sunday
pay	yesterday	subway	Monday
play	weekday	freeway	Tuesday
clay	holiday	driveway	Wednesday
stay	birthday	sideways	Thursday
sway		anyway	Saturday

oa /ō/ Words

oat	oak	boast	coach	blackboard
boat	soak	coast	roach	dashboard
coat	cloak	roast	poach	surfboard
float	croak	toast	approach	skateboard
throat	soap	toaster	cockroach	scoreboard

load	roam	loaf	tugboat
road	foam	meat loaf	steamboat
toad	foamy	oatmeal	sailboat

goal	oar	moan	roadrunner	raincoat
coal	roar	groan	railroad	coatrack

Sail Away on a Rhyming Boat!

NAME _____ DATE _____

Catch a ride on a rhyming sailboat! On each sail below, you will see a list of letters. On the bottom of every boat, you will see a word ending. Add the ending to each of the letters and spell rhyming words. Write your words across the sails.

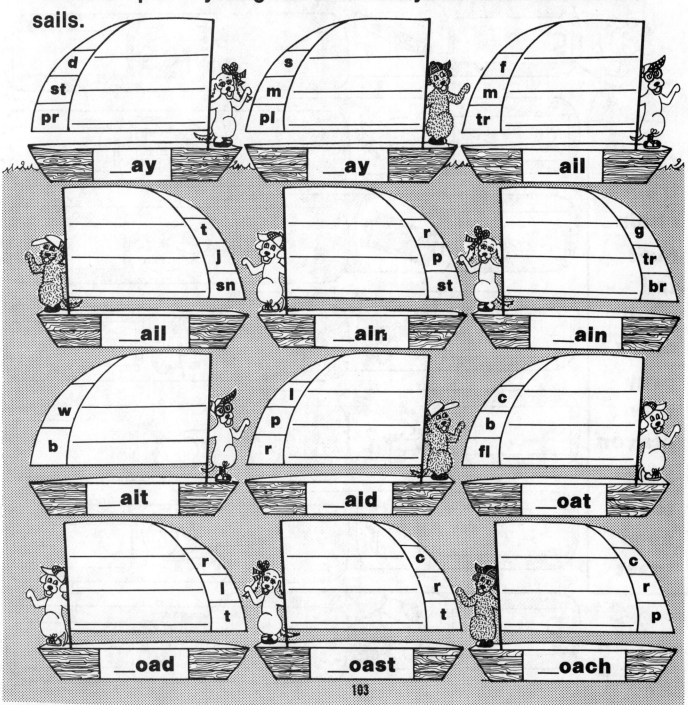

PAINTING WORDS ON BAND-AIDS

NAME _____ DATE _____

On every BAND-AID below, you will see a picture. Find and write the word that will name each picture. Then read all your words to your teacher.

rain
train
chain
mail
tail
snail
daisy
pray
tray
crayon
boat
toad
soap
toast

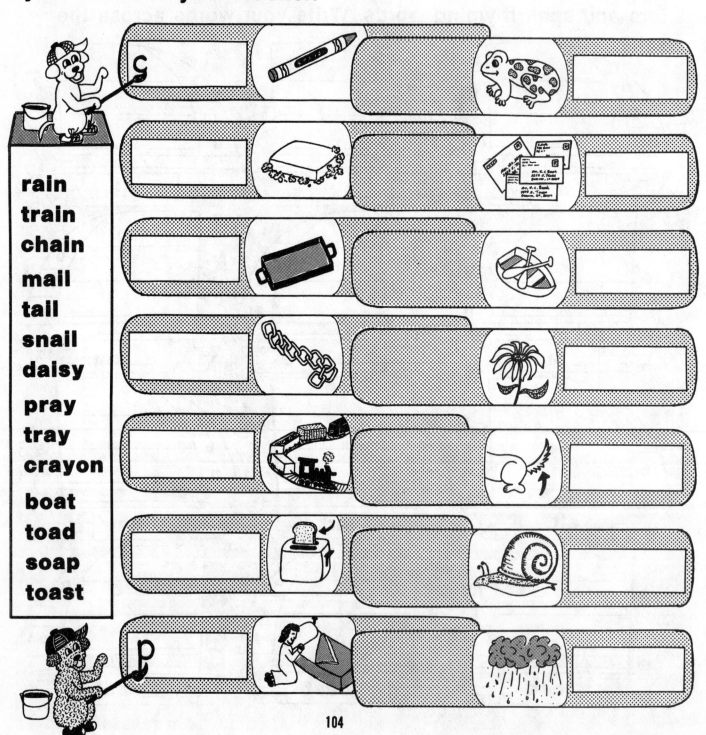

104

CATEGORIES

NAME _____ DATE _____

 Underline all the things below that can be held in your hand.

a tray	a dog's tail
a coat	an empty jail
a toad	a sore throat
a chain	a gray crayon
an oar	a sharp nail
toast	a gravel road
a mermaid	a garden snail
a raindrop	a bar of soap
a subway	a lump of clay
an ashtray	a playful kitten
a railroad	a box of raisins
a raincoat	a moaning mule
a skateboard	your painful feet
a driveway	a bucket of paint
a paycheck	a dish of oatmeal
a rainy day	a bag of mail
a paintbrush	a pan of meat loaf

Coasting Down the Trail on a Hayride Holiday!

NAME _____ DATE _____

🐾 Join the dogs for a hayride holiday! Hop on the hay truck and coast down the trail. You must find and write the word that will complete each sentence along the way.

HAYRIDE TRAIL

A boat can _____.
(fail, float, toast)

When a dog is happy, he will wag his _____.
(brain, tail, throat)

During a wet storm, you may need a _____.
(toad, raincoat, raid)

Cars can drive faster on a _____.
(trail, driveway, freeway)

A hungry horse will eat lots of oats and _____.
(toads, clay, hay)

Your body gets really clean when you use a bar of _____.
(soap, hay, grain)

If you are scared, you must be _____.
(playful, painful, afraid)

A train travels on a _____.
(road, runway, railroad)

This year you will have one more _____.
(mermaid, birthday, blue jay)

You can color with a _____.
(crayon, clay, chain)

If dishes are really dirty, you may have to let them _____.
(roast, play, soak)

Playing with Words on Skateboards!

NAME _____   **DATE** _____

🐾 Join the dogs for a spelling game on skateboards! On
    every skateboard below, you will see words that have
missing vowels. You must find and fill in the right vowel
digraph to spell 2 different words on each skateboard.

Catch That Beaver on the Railroad!

YOU WILL NEED:

2 players
2 gameboard markers
a gameboard (on page 109)
48 game cards (on pages 110 and 111)

1. **Look at the gameboard. A beaver is eating the Dogtown railroad crossing! You must race down the railroad track and help the dogs catch that beaver! One space on the gameboard is between every two railroad ties on the train track.**

2. **Look at the game cards. Each card has a question on it. Cut out all the cards. Put them in a pile face down.**

3. **Place your gameboard markers on the START space.**

4. **Player #1: Draw a game card. Read the question you see and answer it. Player #2 will check you. If the answer to your question is "YES," COUNT THE RAILROAD CROSSING SIGNS on the card. Then move forward that many spaces on the gameboard. If the answer to your question is "NO," you must count the signs on the card and move backwards that many spaces. Player #2: Now you do the same.**

5. **Take turns moving down the railroad track. If you run out of game cards, mix the deck and keep drawing. The first player to reach the railroad crossing will catch that beaver and will WIN the game!**

Catch That Beaver on the Railroad!

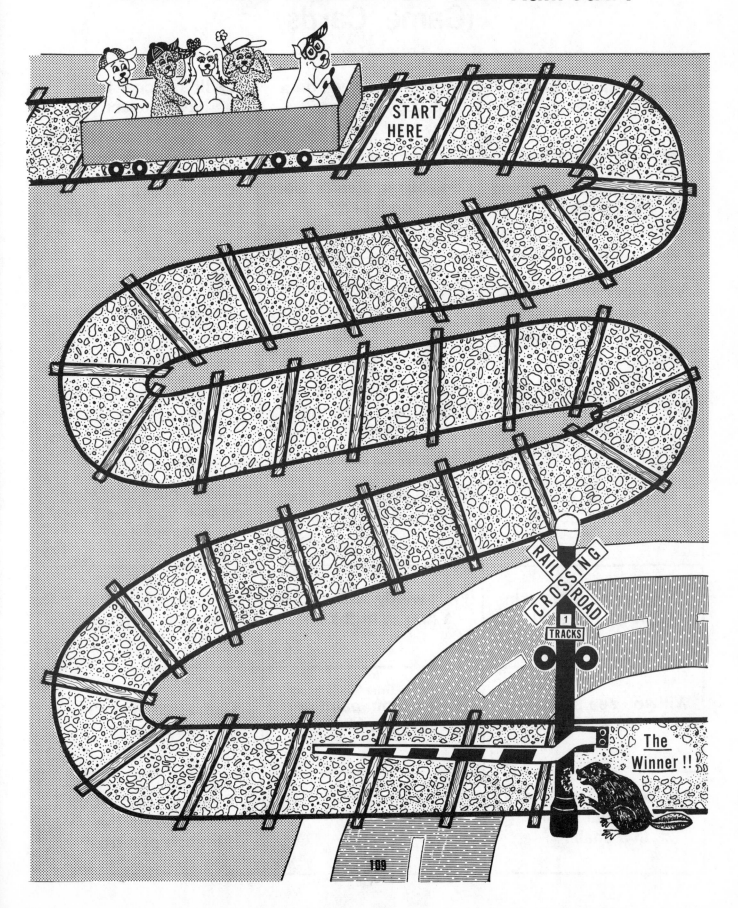

Catch That Beaver on the Railroad!
(Game Cards)

Did you have a birthday last year?	Can a jeep travel on a bumpy dirt road?	Will a soccer team have a coach?
Will a purple snail pop up from a toaster?	Can you put clean sheets on a bed?	Can you slip a pair of sandals onto your feet?
Will meat stay fresh if you freeze it?	Can you hike up a steep trail?	Can you plant a daisy seed in a garden?
Can you eat sweet peas and green beans with a fork?	Will cars, trucks, and buses have steering wheels?	Can you squeeze a soft lump of gray clay?
Can you play Hide and Seek?	Will a rubber raft float across a deep stream?	Will your teeth stay clean if you brush them every day?
Can you peel the skin off of a peach?	If it is windy, will you feel a breeze in the air?	Can you mail sixteen letters?
Will you see steel bars in a jail?	Can a mom paint her fingernails?	Can a hen lay candy Easter eggs?
Can a dad sleep and dream while he sits in a chair?	Can you eat raisins?	Can you hang a bird feeder on the branch of a tree?

Catch That Beaver on the Railroad!
(Game Cards)

Can a bird pick up a leaf with its beak?	Can a coach teach a team to play a game?	Can you feed crackers and cheese to geese?
Can you wait for an airplane at the airport?	Will a can of spray paint scream?	Can you lie on top of a pile of hay?
Can a bumblebee roar?	Can a snake pay for a ticket to the fair?	Can a man take a pair of blue jeans to the cleaners?
Can a teacher dive into a dish of hot oatmeal?	Can three sheep sleep inside a beehive?	Can a mean flea bite a dog's ear?
If it is a sunny day, will you see rain?	Can you drive a boat into an ashtray?	Can a goat read a long story to you?
Can a green crayon explode?	Can a cat stray away from its home?	Will a horse eat oats and hay?
Can you clean dirty feet with a bar of soap?	Can a blue jay sit on the branch of a peach tree?	Can a hot stove heat a platter of meat?
Will a beaver use his sharp teeth to eat the bark of a tree?	Can a toad leap into a creek?	Can a train car be loaded with coal?

111

LET'S TALK ABOUT
the <u>2</u> Sounds of ◉◉

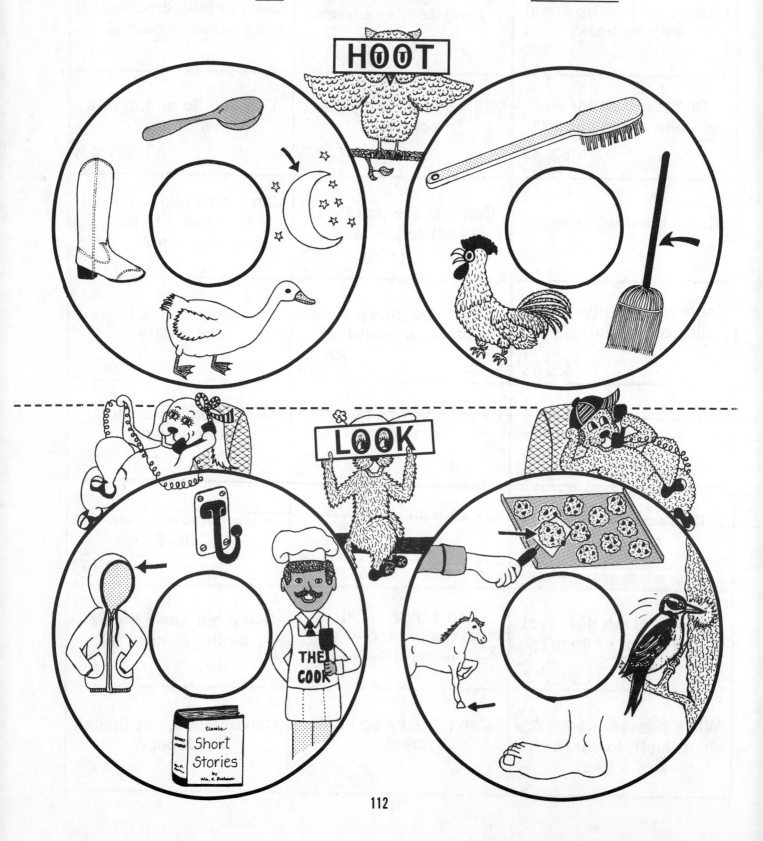

HOOT

LOOK

Words to Read and Spell

Boo!
moo
too
zoo

moon
noon
soon
spoon

goof
roof
proof

tooth
booth
smooth

food

spook

boom
doom
loom
room
zoom
bloom
broom
groom
gloom

hoop
loop
whoop
droop
scoop
stoop
snoop
swoop

boot
hoot
toot
loot
root
shoot
scoot
scooter

cool
fool
tool
pool
spool
school
stool
drool

goose
noose
moose
loose

soothe
ooze

boost
booster

roost
rooster

afternoon
teaspoon

bootee
zookeeper

poodle
noodle
doodle

raccoon
baboon
cocoon

toothbrush
toothpick
toothpaste

boomerang
broomstick
roommate

moody
gloomy
roomy
snoopy
goofy
spooky

igloo
tattoo
bamboo
shampoo
cockatoo
kangaroo

bedroom
bathroom
classroom
mushroom
bridegroom

foolish
toadstool
whirlpool

Words to Read and Spell

book
hook
look
took
cook
nook
brook
crook
shook

good
wood
hood
stood

hoof

wool

woolly
woolen

goody
goodness

cooky
cooker

booklet
bookshelf
bookcase
bookkeeper
bookmark

foot
footstep
footpath
footprint
footstool

understood

barefoot

checkbook
pocketbook
notebook
textbook

woodchuck
woodcutter
woodpecker
woodpile

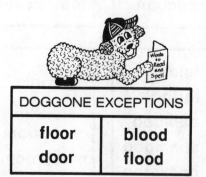

DOGGONE EXCEPTIONS	
floor	blood
door	flood

Choose a Sound on a Footstool

NAME _____ DATE _____

🐾 On every footstool below, you will see a picture and a word spelled with an **oo**. If the **oo** in the word says /o͞o/, as in **moon**, circle the moon. If the **oo** says /o͝o/, as in **book**, circle the book.

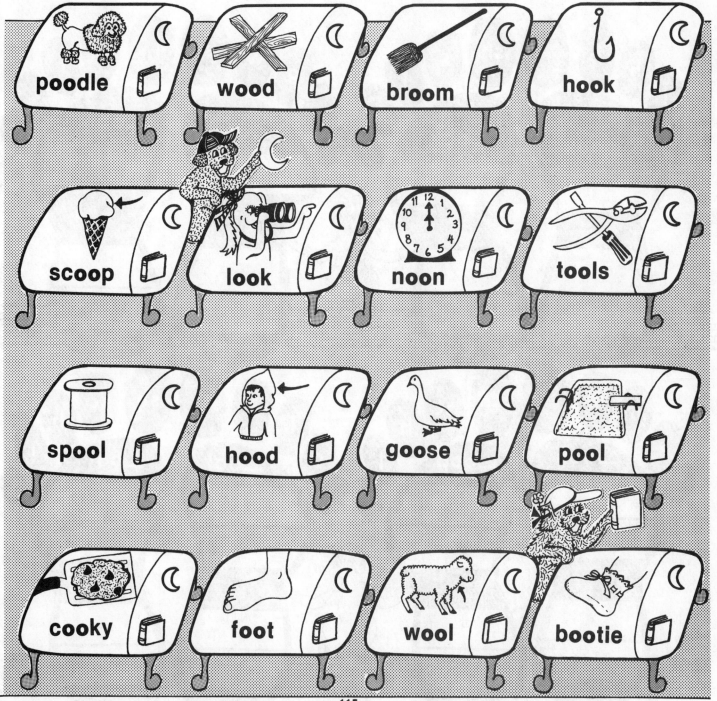

poodle

wood

broom

hook

scoop

look

noon

tools

spool

hood

goose

pool

cooky

foot

wool

bootie

Make Room for Rhyming Footprints!

NAME _____ DATE _____

🐾 On every footprint below, you will see a group of letters and a word ending. Add the ending to each of the letters and spell rhyming words! Then read all your words to your teacher.

Vowel Diphthongs

Special Sounds to Remember

ou *says* /ou/.

ow *can say* /ou/.

ou — house

ou — couch

ou

ow — owl

ow — cow

ow

Words to Read and Spell

ou /ou/ Words

out	bound	our	noun	greenhouse
about	found	sour	mount	tree house
trout	hound	flour	count	playhouse
shout	round		county	
scout	sound	foul	counter	housewife
stout	pound		account	houseboat
spout	mound	house	discount	mousetrap
sprout	ground	mouse	thousand	
		blouse		playground
loud	ouch	spouse	around	underground
aloud	pouch		surround	thundercloud
cloud	couch	outfit		
proud		outside	DOGGONE EXCEPTIONS	
	mouth	outline	would / could / should	you / your
loudly	south	outhouse		
proudly				

ow /ou/ Words

bow	down	owl	tower	sundown
cow	town	howl	flower	countdown
now	gown	growl	shower	splashdown
how	clown			
plow	drown	prowl	power	downtown
chow	frown	prowler	powerful	downstairs
brow	brown			
allow	crown	towel	coward	however
		crowd	powder	browse
		crowded	chowder	drowsy

120

Rhyming Words on Proud Owls

NAME _____ DATE _____

🐾 On every owl below, you will see a word ending and several letters. Add the ending to each of the letters and spell rhyming words! Read all your words to your teacher.

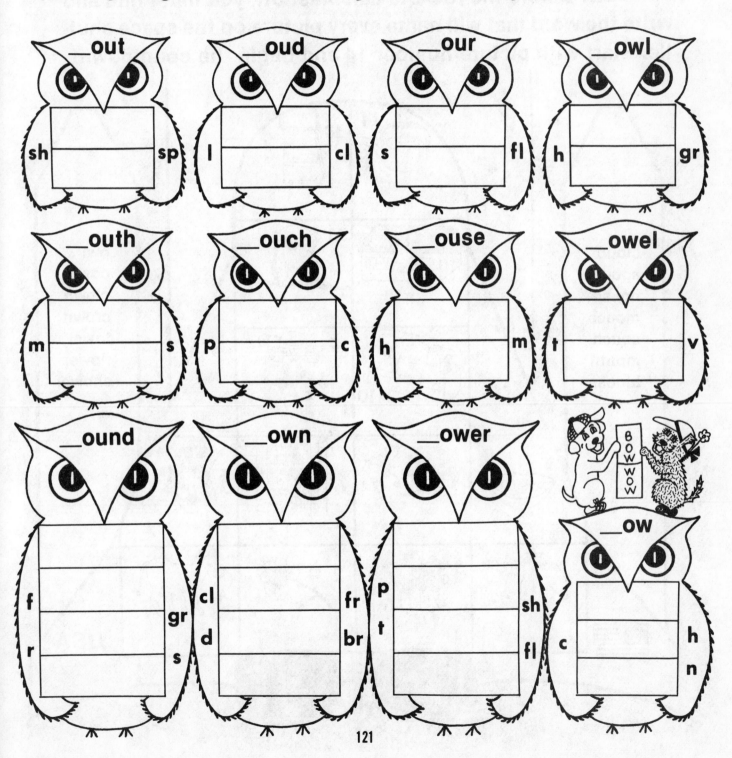

__out   sh   sp

__oud   l   cl

__our   s   fl

__owl   h   gr

__outh   m   s

__ouch   p   c

__ouse   h   m

__owel   t   v

__ound   f   gr   r   s

__own   cl   gr   d

__ower   fr   br

__ow   p   t   sh   fl

__ow   c   h   n

BOW WOW

121

Countdown Before Liftoff!

NAME _____ DATE _____

🐾 There are 14 seconds left before the space shuttle lift-off! Before the rockets can blast off, you must find and write the word that will name every picture on the space shuttle. Start with picture number 14 and begin the countdown!

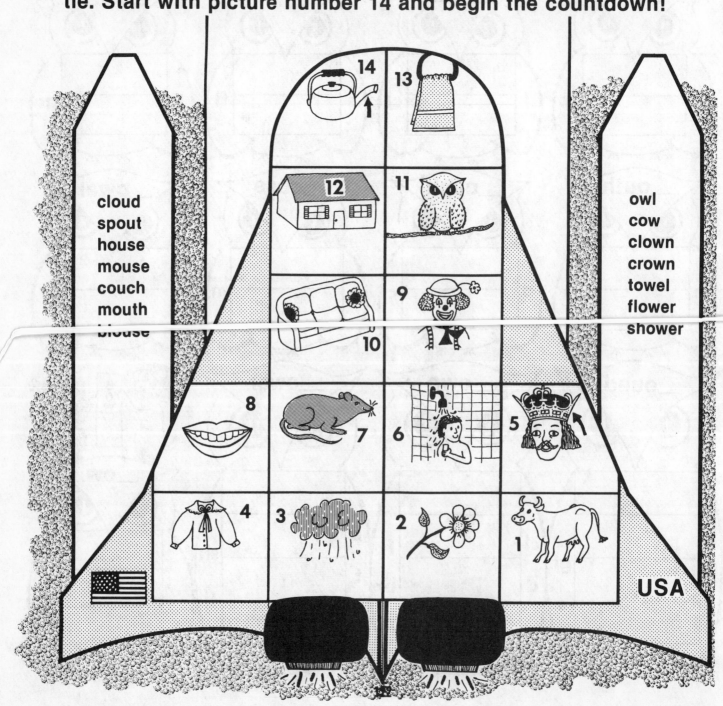

cloud
spout
house
mouse
couch
mouth
blouse

owl
cow
clown
crown
towel
flower
shower

Dogtown's Trout Roundup!

NAME _____ **DATE** _____

Welcome to the Trout Roundup . . . a fishing contest held every year in Dogtown! To win, you must catch all the trout below. To catch each fish, find and fill in the word that will complete every sentence.

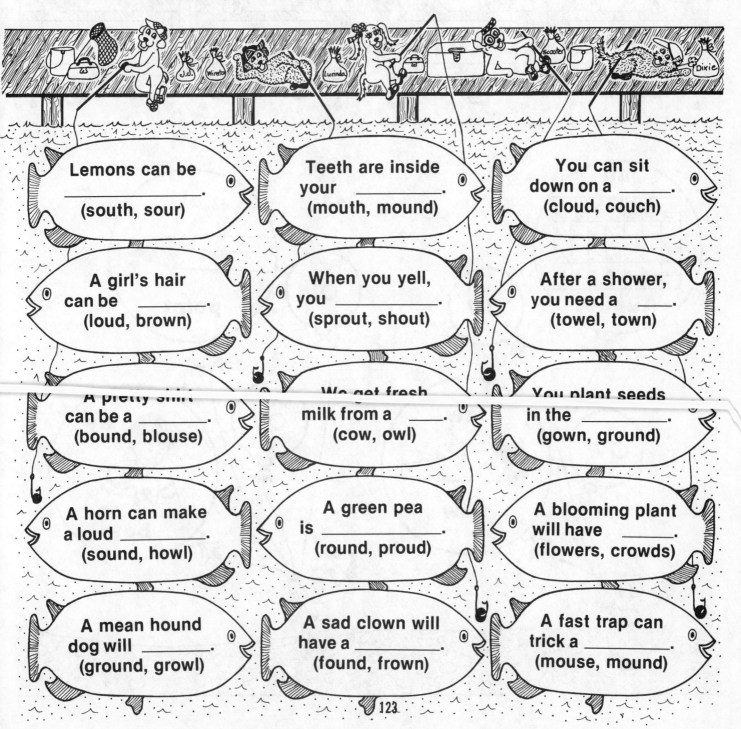

Lemons can be
_____.
(south, sour)

Teeth are inside
your _____.
(mouth, mound)

You can sit
down on a _____.
(cloud, couch)

A girl's hair
can be _____.
(loud, brown)

When you yell,
you _____.
(sprout, shout)

After a shower,
you need a ____.
(towel, town)

A pretty shirt
can be a _____.
(bound, blouse)

We get fresh
milk from a ____.
(cow, owl)

You plant seeds
in the _____.
(gown, ground)

A horn can make
a loud _____.
(sound, howl)

A green pea
is _____.
(round, proud)

A blooming plant
will have _____.
(flowers, crowds)

A mean hound
dog will _____.
(ground, growl)

A sad clown will
have a _____.
(found, frown)

A fast trap can
trick a _____.
(mouse, mound)

123

Vowel Diphthongs
Special Sounds to Remember

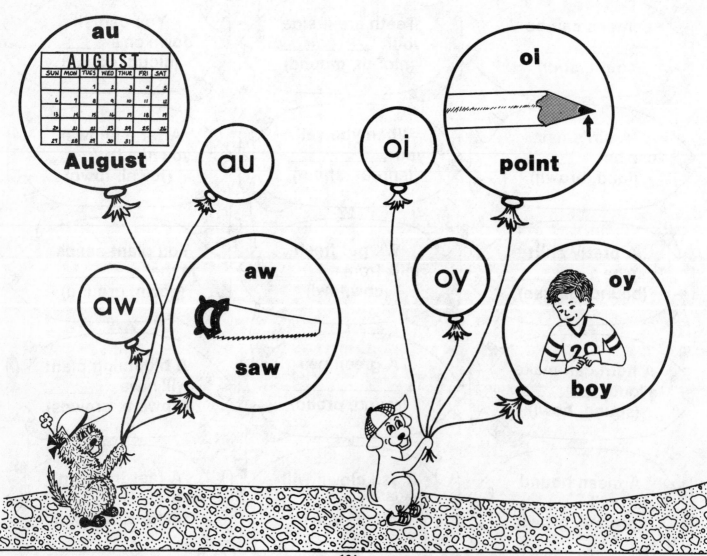

Words to Read and Spell

au /ô/ Words

haul Paul	flaunt	gauze	August author autumn
fault vault	haunt haunted	cause because	laundry
fraud	launch		

aw /ô/ Words

jaw paw raw saw law flaw claw slaw. straw	dawn fawn lawn pawn yawn drawn	pawprint pawnshop
		outlaw lawyer
	crawl shawl	seesaw coleslaw
hawk	awful awning	strawberry

Words to Read and Spell

oi /oi/ Words

oil	coin	hoist	ointment
boil	join	moist	appointment
coil	groin		disappointed
foil			
soil	joint	noise	topsoil
broil	point	noisy	tenderloin
spoil			
	appoint	poison	oily
void	disappoint	toilet	doily

oy /oi/ Words

boy	loyal	cowboy
toy	royal	tomboy
joy		corduroy
enjoy	convoy	soybean
joyful	employ	

126

Enjoy a Rhyming Seesaw Ride!

NAME _____ DATE _____

🐾 Join the dogs for a spelling game on seesaws! The dogs
will show you a word ending and a group of letters. Add
the ending to each of the letters and spell rhyming words!
Write your words on the seesaws. Then read all your words to
your teacher.

Hauling Words in a Convoy!

NAME _____ DATE _____

 Join the convoy and help the dogs haul the right words! Find and write the word that will name each picture on the trucks.

boy
toys

coin
point
toilet

paw
saw
hawk
claw
fawn
shawl
straw
strawberry

August

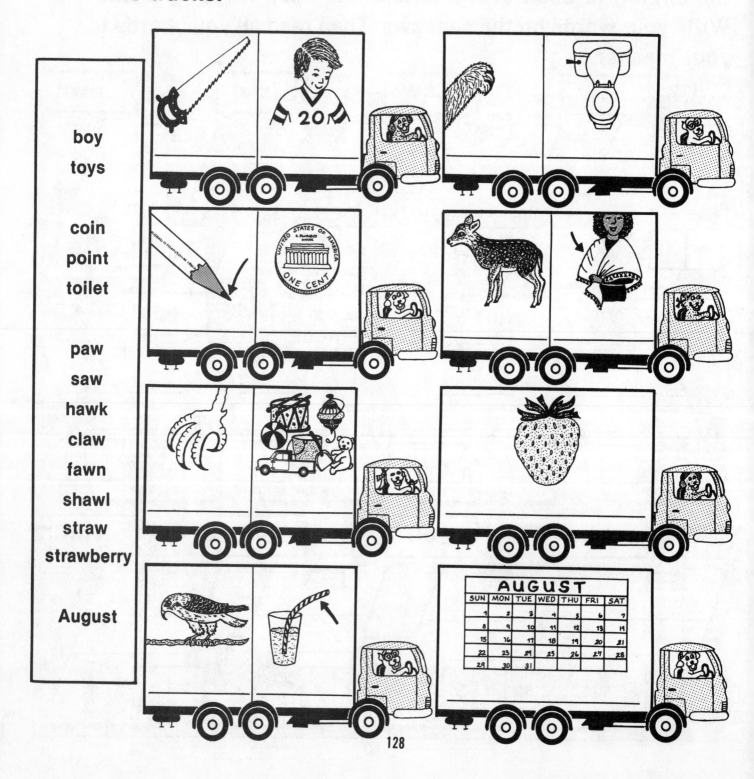

128

Paws Pointing to the Strawberry Patch!

NAME _____ DATE _____

Pick and eat fresh strawberries with the dogs today! Just follow the pawprints and meet the dogs at Farmer Foy's Strawberry Patch. On your way, you must read and answer every question on the path. Write "yes" or "no" in each blank.

Is August a summer month? _____

Can a dog have nine paws? _____

Can you yawn? _____

Can you feel awful? _____

Will a hawk have claws? _____

Can you point your finger? _____

Can a man saw a log? _____

Can you boil an egg? _____

Can soil be moist? _____

Can a truck haul hay? _____

Can a little boy crawl? _____

Can you flip a coin? _____

Can a boy enjoy a toy? _____

Can you drink with a straw? _____

· Farmer · Foy's · Strawberry · Patch ·

Can a cowboy ride a horse? _____

Will the sun rise at dawn? _____

Can a lawn be green? _____

Can a classroom be noisy? _____

CATEGORIES

NAME _____ DATE _____

1. With a brown crayon, underline all the things below that you might find in a bathroom.

2. With a green crayon, underline all the things below that you might find in a kitchen.

3. With a blue crayon, underline all the things below that you might find in a classroom.

a flag	a good teacher
a stove	lots of good food
a skillet	a bottle of shampoo
a toilet	a steaming teapot
a shower	a brown bath towel
bath oil	a boiling coffeepot
tinfoil	a can of mushrooms
a cookbook	a carton of cool milk
math games	lots of spelling books
body powder	boys and girls reading
a cookie jar	a tube of toothpaste
a chalkboard	many boxes of crayons
a toothbrush	a flower for a teacher
a bar of soap	a can of shaving cream
a proud cook	a pound of ground beef
a wooden spoon	lots of desks and chairs
a dish towel	a jar of strawberry jam
a sack of flour	a toaster on a counter top

LET'S TALK ABOUT
Words that Have a Long O /ō/ Sound

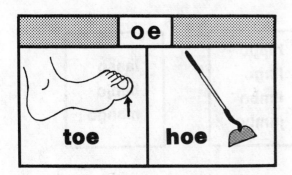

oe

toe   hoe

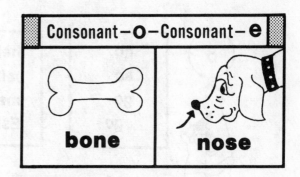

Consonant—**o**—Consonant—**e**

bone   nose

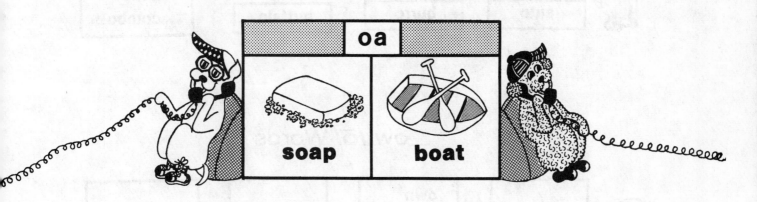

oa

soap   boat

OW can say /ō/.

OW

bowl   crow

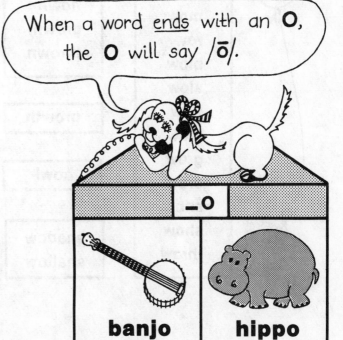

When a word _ends_ with an **O**, the **O** will say /ō/.

_o

banjo   hippo

Words to Read and Spell

__o /ō/ Words

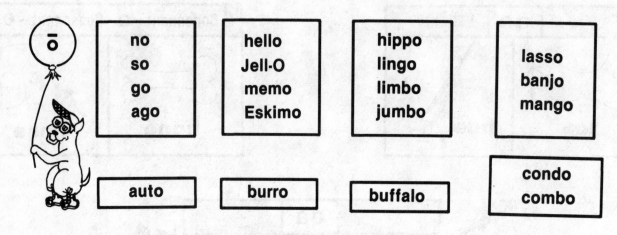

no	hello	hippo	lasso
so	Jell-O	lingo	banjo
go	memo	limbo	mango
ago	Eskimo	jumbo	

auto	burro	buffalo	condo
			combo

__ow /ō/ Words

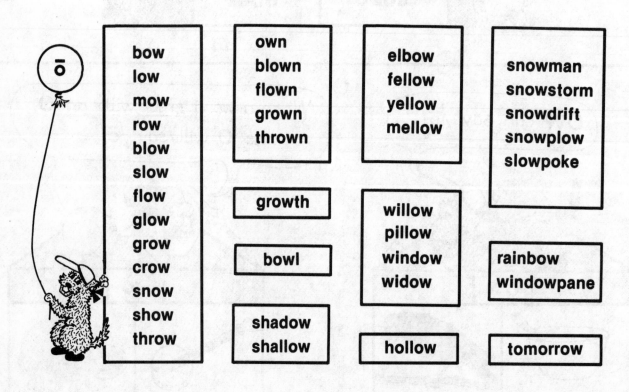

bow	own	elbow	snowman
low	blown	fellow	snowstorm
mow	flown	yellow	snowdrift
row	grown	mellow	snowplow
blow	thrown		slowpoke
slow			
flow	growth	willow	
glow		pillow	
grow	bowl	window	rainbow
crow		widow	windowpane
snow			
show	shadow		
throw	shallow	hollow	tomorrow

132

Glowing Candles in the Dark

NAME_____ DATE_____

 Find and write the word that will name every picture on the candles below. Read all your words to your teacher.

a bow	a banjo	an elbow	a yellow crayon
a crow	a hippo	a window	a lawn mower
a bowl	a buffalo	a rainbow	a slow turtle
a pillow	an Eskimo	a rowboat	a snowman

133

Take a Burro to Mexico!

NAME _____ DATE _____

Join the dogs for a reading ride to Mexico! Hop onto a burro and follow the road! On the way, you must read and answer every question. Write "yes" or "no" on each blank.

Can you blow out ten candles? _____
Were you born twenty years ago? _____

If it is sunny outside, will you see your shadow? _____
Can the wind blow hard during a snowstorm? _____

Can you throw a beanbag? _____
Can you sit on a soft pillow? _____

Can flowers grow? _____
Can you tie a bow? _____

Can a creek be shallow? _____
Are lemons yellow? _____

Can a boy own a bike? _____
Can a hippo mow your lawn? _____

Can you eat a Jell-O salad? _____
Can you look out the window? _____

Can a car go slow? _____
Is a crow a bird? _____

THE BORDER OF MEXICO

LET'S TALK ABOUT
the Sounds of <u>Y</u>

Y will say /y/ when it is the <u>first</u> letter in a word.

y /y/

yarn

yellow

Sometimes Y will say /ē/.

y /ē/

puppy

20 **twenty**

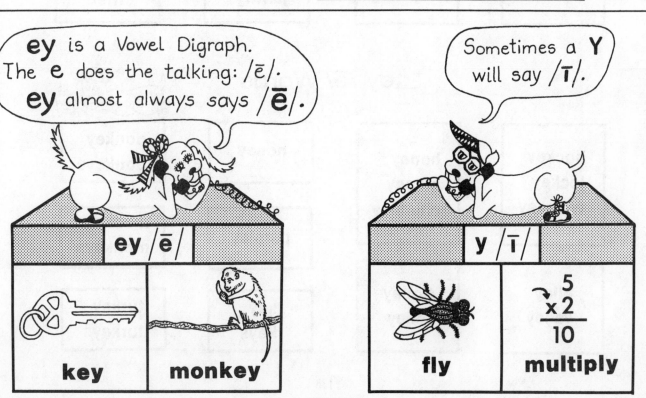

ey is a Vowel Digraph. The **e** does the talking: /ē/. **ey** almost always says /ē/.

ey /ē/

key

monkey

Sometimes a **Y** will say /ī/.

y /ī/

fly

$$\begin{array}{r} 5 \\ \times 2 \\ \hline 10 \end{array}$$

multiply

Words to Read and Spell

y /ī/ Words

by	bye	nearby	fly
my	lye	lullaby	flies
why	rye	good-bye	
shy	type		try
fly	style	butterfly	tries
dry	rhyme	firefly	tried
fry			
cry	flying	supply	cry
try	drying	multiply	cries
sky	crying		cried
spy	trying	satisfy	
	frying	magnify	fry
dryer	typing	testify	fries
	rhyming	justify	fried

_ey /ē/ Words

hockey	honey	nosey	donkey
jockey	money		donkeys
whiskey	chimney	parsley	
			monkey
alley	trolley	key	monkeys
valley	volley	keys	
			turkey
			turkeys

136

Dogtown's Auto Giveaway!

NAME _____ **DATE** _____

You have just picked the winning ticket for Dogtown's Auto Giveaway! If you can find and write the word that names each picture on the keys, you will win a brand-new sports car . . . FREE!

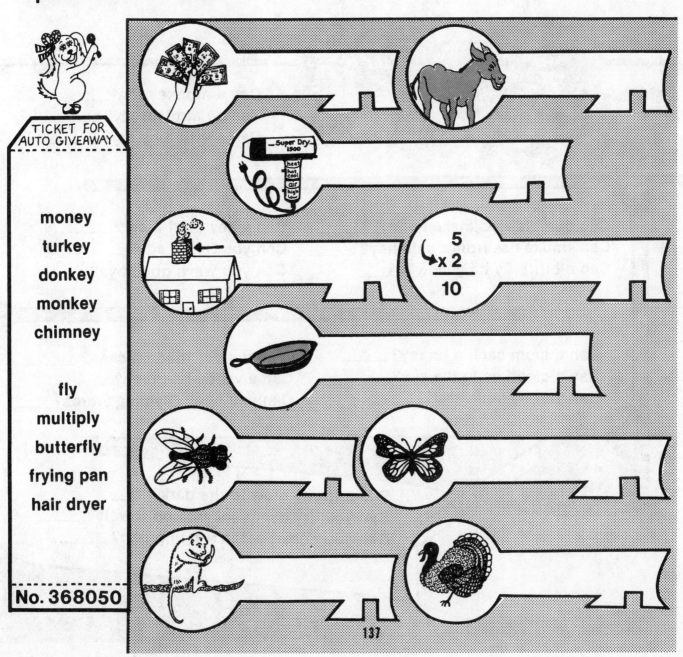

TICKET FOR AUTO GIVEAWAY

money

turkey

donkey

monkey

chimney

fly

multiply

butterfly

frying pan

hair dryer

No. 368050

137

Run for the Money!

NAME _____ DATE _____

Welcome to the Dogtown Racetrack. The jockey who wins this race will get three thousand dollars! So hop on a fast horse and run for the money! To win the money, you must answer every question on the track correctly. Write "yes" or "no" on each blank.

Can a monkey fly? _____
Can an airplane fly? _____
Can a little boy cry? _____

Can bumblebees make honey? _____
Can smoke rise from a chimney? _____
Can a butterfly be yellow? _____

Can a key start a car? _____
Can you fry an egg? _____
Can you wave good-bye? _____

Can a mom cook a turkey? _____
Can a cloud be in the sky? _____
Can you try your best? _____

Can you eat fried chicken? _____
Can a valley be green? _____
Can you spell rhyming words? _____

FINISH

Will a firefly glow in the dark? _____
Can you dry damp sheets and towels? _____
Can you cook beef in a frying pan? _____

LET'S TALK ABOUT

Words that Have an <u>Open</u> <u>Syllable</u>

An **open syllable** is a **word part** that **ends** with a **single vowel.**

That single vowel will be long.

no **go** **so**	**be** **we** **me**	**he** **she**	These are one-syllable words. They are open syllables. Each word ends with a single vowel. That **single vowel** is **long.**

Sometimes 2-part words will contain an open syllable. The words below begin with open syllables.

$\bar{a}$	$\bar{e}$	$\bar{\imath}$	$\bar{o}$	$\bar{u}$
ba•by baby	be•gin begin	ti•ger tiger	ho•tel hotel	mu•sic music
pa•per paper	fe•ver fever	si•lent silent	po•ny pony	tu•lip tulip

The first part of every word above is an open syllable. The first syllable of each word ends with a single vowel. That vowel has a long sound.

Words to Read and Spell

$\bar{a}$

lady	able	paper	apron
shady	cable	wafer	bacon
baby	table	cater	basin
navy	stable	later	raven
wavy	cradle	razor	vacant
gravy	ladle	laser	
crazy	staple	flavor	radio
lazy	maple	major	stadium
hazy			
tasty	label	halo	apricot
shaky	hazel		

$\bar{e}$

zebra	fever	pretend	relax
zero	secret	prevent	refund
hero	create	prepare	refresh
veto		preschool	request
			respect
			retire
even	begin	demon	refuse
evil	begun	deliver	report
eleven	beyond	demand	return
eleventh	belong	depend	reverse
electric	became	defend	repeat
elastic	behave	defense	repair
equipment	beware	defrost	reply
	before	define	
elect	between	develop	reflex
erase	beneath	destroy	remember
	because		

Words to Read and Spell

ī

idea ideal iris ivy item ivory	title Bible rifle idle bridle	sinus siren silent	triangle tripod trial
		lion lilac	hijack hibernate
spider tiger minor	tiny tidy Friday	diet quiet pilot	

ō

open only over oval	local locust locate rotate donate	sober solar solo soda cola	poet poem	bony pony
			robot romantic	program protest protect profile provide pronoun
hotel motel motor moment	bonus focus frozen	noble yodel yogurt	polite polio rodeo	

ū

unit unite uniform	ruby duty	tulip tumor tutor tuna	super humor human humid	ruin fluid stupid pupil
	music			
bugle	July			

Prepare for the Super-Duper Tasty Diet Cola Contest!

NAME _____ DATE _____

You have just picked the winning ticket for Dogtown's Super-Duper Tasty Diet Cola Contest! If you can find and write the word that will name every picture on the cola bottles, you will **win** thirty cases of diet cola . . . FREE! Write your words on the bottles.

spider
tiger
lion

apron
razor
table
radio
paper
baby
stapler
lady

eraser
zero
eleven

music
bugle
tulip
pony

No. 86910

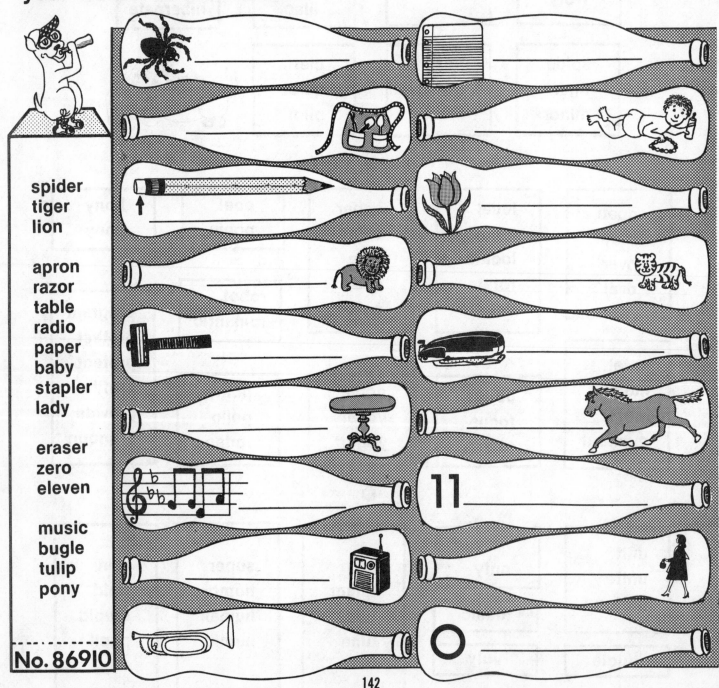

142

Rest and Relax at the Dogtown Motel

NAME _____ DATE _____

🐾 Let's pretend that you just arrived in Dogtown and you need a place to stay. The local Dogtown Motel is really fun, and the dogs are there . . . waiting to greet you! Just follow Maple Street. Be sure to answer every question along the way. Write "yes" or "no" on the blanks.

Maple Street

Can a pony tell a secret to a pretty lady? _____
Will a man in the navy have a uniform? _____
Will a mailman deliver lots of letters? _____
Will a horse eat hay in a quiet stable? _____

Will music be on the radio? _____
Can you eat turkey and gravy? _____
Will a baby sleep in a cradle? _____
Can you erase on paper? _____

Can lions roar? _____
Can a tiger yawn? _____
Can poems rhyme? _____
Can a cow be lazy? _____

Can frozen meat be defrosted? _____
Is frozen yogurt refreshing? _____
Can you prepare for a party? _____
Can you open a window? _____

Can you set a table? _____
Can you have an idea? _____
Can a pilot fly a jet? _____
Can you belong to a club? _____

DOGTOWN MOTEL

Can a mom diet? _____
Can a baby crawl? _____
Can a spider bite? _____

Eeny, Meeny, Miney, Moe, Choose a Sound and Make Words Grow!

NAME _____   DATE _____

On every windmill below, you will see a word with missing letters. Find the letters that can be used to complete the words. Pick three different letter choices to spell three different words across the windmills. Then read all your words to your teacher.

CATEGORIES

NAME _____ DATE _____

 Underline anything below that describes an animal.

a burro	a roaring lion
a moose	a little fawn
a donkey	a bunny rabbit
a raccoon	a rattlesnake
a dentist	a good teacher
an artist	a furry monkey
a wise owl	a playful kitten
a lazy cow	a shaggy puppy
a big baboon	a stubborn mule
a mailman	a riding cowboy
a sly fox	a frisky squirrel
a baby hippo	a pretty peacock
a shiny seal	a crawling snail
a soccer coach	an angry buffalo
a mean bobcat	a crowing rooster
a happy clown	a galloping horse
a blue whale	a croaking toad
a soft towel	a hopping kangaroo
a slow turtle	a little gray mouse
a yellow flower	a proud chimpanzee
a thirsty camel	nickels and dimes
a striped zebra	a very smart poodle
a sleeping tiger	a lucky fisherman

CATEGORIES

NAME _____ DATE _____

 1. With a red crayon, underline all the foods below.

2. With a green crayon, underline ways that a person can feel.

tuna	ripe peaches
smart	frozen yogurt
bored	clam chowder
happy	butter cookies
afraid	weak and sore
moody	chicken potpie
lonely	cream style corn
cherries	safe and sound
awful	angry and upset
mellow	blueberry pancakes
meat loaf	brave and daring
confused	tired and grumpy
coleslaw	oatmeal with raisins
grateful	hungry and thirsty
homesick	relaxed and rested
fantastic	grape jelly on toast
dill pickles	clean and refreshed
really well	surprised and shocked
very proud	a bowl of strawberries
Jell-O salad	peppy and very cheerful
lima beans	roast beef and brown gravy
bean sprouts	a cheeseburger and French fries